Test Bank

to accompany

Smith

Breaking Through
College Reading
Sixth Edition

Linda L. Arthur

Georgia Southern University

Longman

New York Boston San Francisco
London Toronto Sydney Tokyo Singapore Madrid
Mexico City Munich Paris Cape Town Hong Kong Montreal

NOTE REGARDING WEBSITES AND PASSWORDS

If you need a password to access instructor supplements on a Longman book-specific Website, use the following information:

Username: awlbook
Password: adopt

Test Bank to accompany Smith, *Breaking Through: College Reading, Sixth Edition*

Copyright ©2002 Pearson Education, Inc.
Publishing as Longman Publishers.

ISBN: 0-321-05106-8

1 2 3 4 5 6 7 8 9 10-DM-04 03 02 01

TABLE OF CONTENTS

PREFACE

Within this volume the instructor will find assessment material to accompany Smith's *Breaking Through: College Reading*. The tests are constructed to measure the student's ability to: 1) comprehend chapter content through multiple-choice and true-false items; 2) apply reading skills to supplemental reading passages; 3) demonstrate reading comprehension through writing; 4) apply test-taking strategies; 5) study college textbooks efficiently; and 6) think and read critically. In addition, students are required to preview, annotate, interpret, evaluate, and synthesize reading selections.

Features of the test bank include:

A. Approximately two to three tests for each chapter: a multiple-choice test of ten or twenty items is presented in eleven of the twelve chapters; these tests are beneficial in that they facilitate scoring.

B. Two Mastery Tests:

   Mastery Test I assesses whether or not the student has a grasp of the content of Chapters One through Six. It covers basic terminology and the academic reading skills of main idea, details, organizational patterns, and vocabulary.

   Mastery Test II determines whether or not the student has learned the content of Chapters Seven through Eleven. Test-Taking Strategies must be applied, and the higher academic reading skills of analytical reasoning, inference, and critical reading are tested.

C. An independent textbook assignment for demonstrating annotating skills (Chapter Twelve).

D. Tests which help determine the student's reading rate and comprehension of questions under timed testing situations.

E. Reading selections which were carefully selected to reflect the concepts presented in the chapters as well as to reflect course content across the curriculum. Passages were drawn from such disciplines as philosophy and religion, business, psychology, health science, communication arts, political science, and sociology.

F. Answer keys

CHAPTER ONE: Student Success

TEST A

Answer the multiple-choice questions based on the content of the chapter.

1. According to the text, the most important factor for a successful college experience is

a. obtaining a high school diploma.
b. maintaining a passing grade-point average.
c. an attitude for success.

2. Les Brown, a prominent motivational speaker, advocates

a. not neglecting partying while pursuing greatness.
b. staying focused on goals.
c. making compromises to achieve goals.

3. The way successful people manage to get more done is that they

a. keep a To Do list.
b. have lunch regularly with successful businessmen.
c. work on Saturday.

4. A "To Do" list

a. should be reworked at the end of the day.
b. enumerates mostly C-priority items.
c. should not be used as a daily guide to action.

5. All of the following are activities for creating an effective learning plan *except*

a. taking a close look at all syllabi.
b. completing a detailed calendar.
c. adopting a "slow start" strategy.

6. It can be inferred from the text that

a. a student gets out of a class what she or he puts into it.
b. students should expect the professor to dominate the class.
c. students do not need to attend class to succeed.

7. According to the text, attending class the first day is crucial because

a. a student always impresses the professor by coming the first day.
b. class goals are usually explained on that day.
c. students meet future friends.

8. According to the text, all of the following are keys to academic success *except*

a. currying favor with the professor.
b. reading the syllabus.
c. attending class.

9. Students should review lecture notes to solidify learning

a. only before a test.
b. once a week.
c. after each class session.

10. It has been shown through studies that networking is important because

a. students are able to make social bonds.
b. a smaller number of students drop out of college when they have a support system.
c. younger students meet older students who can help them.

11. Having a "study buddy" is advantageous because

a. "A" students are always willing to let you copy their work.
b. students can divide work loads efficiently.
c. students can learn how to e-mail messages to their buddies.

12. Techniques for effective studying include all of the following *except*

a. watching videos related to topics being studied.
b. predicting exam questions.
c. listening to all taped lectures the night before the test.

13. According to Phillip C. McGraw, life rewards

a. thoughts backed by actions.
b. procrastination.
c. thoughts without actions.

14. One of the main points of this chapter is

a. always imitate your professor's behavior.
b. life rarely rewards college students.
c. to become a winner, think like a winner.

15. The Internet is an electronic system

a. developed by the United States Department of Education.
b. of more than 25,000 computer networks.
c. that was developed in the 1990s by Bill Gates.

16. The author compares Web sites to

a. books.
b. pages of a newspaper.
c. photographic material.

17. A Web site's home page is like a

a. Web address.
b. directory path.
c. main terminal.

18. You can get an overview of a Web site by doing all of the following *except*

a. typing in the URL.
b. viewing the graphics.
c. scanning the headline.

19. Clicking on Hypertext Links can

a. send you to related web sites.
b. link you to the current web site's home page.
c. refer you to bold, blue text.

20. Search engines

a. do not include Yahoo or Excite.
b. look through the entire Internet for information on your topic.
c. are continually breaking down and consequently are not very useful.

TEST B: ESSAY

You will be writing one essay. Read the introductory paragraphs, then choose <u>one</u> of the questions (either A or B) to write about. Be sure to support your opinion or points with examples.

Optimism, a positive state of mind, is really more an outlook, a view that has to do with how you explain the bad things that happen in your life, which in turn can keep you from becoming depressed or demoralized in the face of setbacks. In failing an exam, for example, some people would say they failed because they are stupid. They explain it in terms of some fixed, permanent trait in themselves. (That's the negative or pessimistic view.) Others would say they failed because it was a very hard test, but next time they'll study harder. They explain bad things happening in terms of a constantly changing situation-not a permanent flaw within themselves. They are hopeful that things will be different next time.

In one study started in the 1940s, students at Harvard University were classified as pessimists or optimists based on essays they had written explaining events in their lives. About thirty years later, the health history of these same students was examined. Starting in their forties, the pessimists had more serious diseases and health problems than the optimists.

-Goleman, 1997, pp. 40-41

A. How has pessimism blocked you from your dreams in the past? Give three specific examples. Looking back at these situations now, how could an optimistic view have helped you through the situations? That is, how would you have handled the situations differently? Do you believe that a negative outlook in life and/or stressful situations can lead to health problems? Why or why not?

Behavior in the Classroom. Your body has its own language in class and can communicate a lot, even if you rarely say a word. You want to be comfortable, but if you prop your feet up in another desk, lean your head on the wall, or slump forward, you will look inattentive. Avoid sitting back with your arms folded because you obviously aren't taking notes and can even be perceived as aggressive or defiant, especially if you look unhappy and bored.

Use facial expressions and eye contact to demonstrate interest and attention. Watch the teacher unless you are taking notes, and if the teacher catches your eye, don't look away. You can even use body language to participate in class, which can be a particularly helpful technique for the shy or unprepared student. As your teacher or classmates talk, focus on them. Don't fidget. Tapping pens, pointedly looking at your watch, shifting around restlessly in your seat, getting out your keys-this kind of body language is distracting.

Remember to behave as you would if you and the teacher were the only people in the room. You wouldn't stare out the window, fail to respond to a question, or go to sleep, would you? Strive to impress the teacher with your qualities as a student. A pleasant, attentive expression and good posture can go a long way toward making a good impression.

-Arthur, *et. al.*, 1996, pp. 23; 25-26.

B. Try to recall classmates who did not like to go to class. What kind of behaviors did they exhibit to call attention to the fact that they did not like the class? Was the teacher aware that these students did not like the class? At the time, did you consider these students to be "acting successfully"? What kind of grades did they earn? What did you learn from their actions and the consequences of their actions? Be sure to address the question of how you could improve your behavior in the classroom.

CHAPTER TWO: Stages of Reading

TEST A

Answer the multiple-choice questions based on the content of the chapter.

1. Currently, experts believe that reading is

a. the ability to pronounce words fluently.
b. a product of a passive task.
c. an active process.

2. The process of previewing does not involve

a. relating the information to future research.
b. realizing what you already know about the topic.
c. learning what the material is about.

3. Study systems are designed to

a. aid the student in finding a study buddy.
b. engage the reader in thought throughout the reading process.
c. show the student that it is only necessary to preview material.

4. When previewing a textbook, a student would not usually look at

a. the Table of Contents and different kinds of type.
b. indexes and chapter subheadings.
c. critiques of the text by other experts.

5. According to this chapter, the best way to determine whether a book has importance for you is to

a. ask a fellow student.
b. read the title.
c. investigate the background of the author.

6. A visual overview of a chapter

a. enables a student to pass a test without studying.
b. gives students an idea of what the chapter covers.
c. is not a good strategy for previewing a text.

7. While reading, prior knowledge of a subject is

a. not usually utilized.
b. an obstacle.
c. a schema that aids the student.

8. According to the chapter, one obstacle to reading well is

a. not knowing when you are not comprehending.
b. reading out loud in front of the class.
c. trying to integrate new knowledge with prior knowledge.

9. According to Davey, good readers do all of the following *except*

a. make educated guesses.
b. visualize the material.
c. continue reading even if confused.

10. When reading an essay by a college freshman trying to adapt to his/her new environment, you are probably relating to the experience through

a. comparison.
b. prediction.
c. explanation.

11. Experts encourage "recall," which is the third stage of reading, because

a. it is the best stage at which a student can memorize facts.
b. comprehension and memory are improved.
c. students have never been taught to follow through with memorization techniques.

12. The method you will utilize for recalling will depend on

a. your purpose for learning.
b. the professor.
c. how many pages you have to cover.

13. Usually a reader can answer literal questions because

a. the answers to such questions are stated in the selection.
b. they require the student to make an educated guess.
c. they necessitate the most sophisticated level of reading.

14. Main idea and inference questions are examples of

a. applied questions.
b. literal questions.
c. interpretive questions.

15. A good main idea for the section on good readers (pp. 9-14) would be

a. "the only strategy a good reader needs to use to comprehend well is activating a schemata."
b. "there are five strategies good readers utilize."
c. "reading is a difficult process."

16. You can infer from the selection that the author believes reading to be a(n)

a. isolated activity.
b. simplistic activity.
c. integrative process.

17. For studying science, all of the following techniques for remembering information are mentioned in the text *except*

a. skimming.
b. virtual research.
c. mnemonics.

18. According to the author, the best way to reinforce and integrate what you have read is to

a. read, explain, and make a checklist.
b. recall, react, and reflect.
c. use mnemonics, re-read, and pronounce unfamiliar vocabulary words.

19. When reading and studying sociology, a student should

a. search for historical reasons for human behaviors.
b. be intolerant of cultural differences.
c. use the same process as s/he uses in reading and studying biology.

20. A newspaper is organized in such a way that

a. an index is included on the last page of the edition.
b. the most important points are in the first paragraphs of the articles.
c. the first page is composed solely of local news.

TEST B

This test focuses on the ability to preview text material. Pay close attention to any information you find in the photos and figures and to peripheral information as well. Then answer the multiple-choice questions that follow.

FIGURE 1

FIGURE 2

Women have been involved in protest movements throughout the years. Here women march in support of the Equal Rights Amendment. Failure to achieve ratification by the required three-fourths of states sent the amendment to its final defeat in 1982.

-Martin, et. al., 1977, p. 1065

The popular television show "Queen for a Day" reinforced established female sex roles by providing winners with everything they needed to be better housewives. Here, host Jack Bailey crowns a "Queen for a Day."

-Martin, et. al., 1997, p. 1059

1. In Figure 1, ERA

a. is a shortened form of AM<u>ER</u>IC<u>A</u>.
b. stands for Equal Rights Amendment.
c. represents a real estate association.

2. The "Queen for a Day" (Figure 2) received

a. a new home.
b. trophies to designate her new title.
c. gifts to enhance her role as housewife.

FIGURE 3

FIGURE 4

Table 30.4 PERCENTAGE OF FEMALES IN SELECTED OCCUPATIONS

Occupation	1972 (Percentage)	1980 (Percentage)	1989 (Percentage)
Professional/technical	39.3	44.3	45.2
Accountants	21.7	36.2	48.6
Computer specialists	16.8	25.7	35.7
Engineers	0.8	4.0	7.6
Lawyers and judges	3.8	12.8	22.3
Life/physical scientists	10.0	20.3	26.9
Physicians/dentists	9.3	12.9	16.5
Professors	28.0	33.9	38.7
Engineering/science technicians	9.1	17.8	19.2
Writers/artists/entertainers	31.7	39.3	46.0
Sales	41.6	45.3	49.3
Real estate agents/brokers	36.7	50.7	51.0
Clerks, retail	68.9	71.1	81.8
Clerical	75.6	80.1	80.0
Bookkeepers	97.9	90.5	91.7
Clerical supervisors	57.8	70.5	58.2
Office machine operators	71.4	72.6	62.6
Secretaries	99.1	99.1	98.3
Crafts workers	3.6	6.0	8.6
Blue-collar supervisors	6.9	10.8	n/a*
Machinists and jobsetters	0.6	4.0	n/a*
Tool and die makers	0.5	2.8	n/a*
Mechanics (except automobile)	1.0	2.6	3.1

Source: U.S. Bureau of the Census, *Statistical Abstract of the United States: 1982–83* (103d edition), *1991* (111th edition), Washington, D.C., 1982, 1991.
*n/a = not available.

Table 30.5 RATIO OF DIVORCES TO MARRIAGES, 1890—1987

1890	1–17
1900	1–12
1910	1–11
1920	1–7
1930	1–5
1940	1–6
1950	1–4.3
1960	1–3.8
1970	1–3.5
1980	1–2
1987	1–2.1

-Martin, et. al., 1997, p. 1069

-Martin, et. al. , 1997, p. 1068

3. Figure 3 shows that in 1972 the majority of women worked as

a. secretaries.
b. bookkeepers.
c. physicians.

4. In 1989 (Figure 3), the percent of women physicians and dentists had risen from 1972 by about

a. 70%.
b. 16.5%.
c. 7%.

5. In Figure 3 for 1980, it is revealed that the occupation which was least filled by women was

a. engineer.
b. mechanic.
c. tool maker.

6. A reader could infer that the statistics in Figure 4 were found in a textbook for a

a. sociology class.
b. criminal justice class.
c. philosophy and religion.

7. Figure 4 indicates that

a. more people divorced in 1987 than 1890.
b. fewer people divorced in 1960 than 1900.
c. the same number of peopled divorced in 1960 and 1970.

8. An overview of Figures 1 - 4 would suggest that the tables were found in a chapter about

a. careers and hiring practices.
b. political movements.
c. women's liberation.

FIGURE 5

CONTENTS

-Ross, 1994, pp. vii-viii

9. Viewing the Table of Contents (Figure 5) above, which of the following titles would be the most appropriate title for the book in which the Table of Contents appeared?

a. *Treatment for Substance Abuse*
b. *Adolescent Substance Abuse*
c. *Diagnosis and Treatment*

10. Each chapter of this textbook includes

a. a summary.
b. a preface.
c. study questions.

CHAPTER THREE: Vocabulary

TEST A

Answer the multiple-choice questions based on the content of the chapter.

1. A high school graduate recognizes approximately how many words?

a. 50,000
b. 15,000
c. 10,000

2. Association, concept cards, and practicing are ways to

a. recognize context clues.
b. remember new words.
c. increase visualization of words.

3. Directly stating the meaning of an unknown word in a sentence or paragraph is what kind of context clue?

a. elaborating details
b. definition
c. example

4. Finding similar situations in a passage suggests that the context clue is a(n)

a. explanation.
b. contrast.
c. comparison.

5. Which of the following is considered the basic part of a word?

a. prefix
b. root
c. suffix

6. It is advantageous to learn suffixes because a reader will know how a word may be

a. divided into syllables.
b. defined.
c. used in a sentence.

7. If while reading, an unknown word appears, the reader should

a. mark the word, finish reading, and then look up the word in the dictionary.
b. stop reading immediately and look the word up in the dictionary.
c. skim over the word and continue reading.

8. Word origins are also referred to as

a. entries.
b. guide words.
c. etymologies.

9. The glossary of a textbook is found

a. in the front of the book.
b. in the middle of the book.
c. at the end of the book.

10. A thesaurus will not help a writer find

a. antonyms for a word.
b. synonyms for a word.
c. origins of a word.

11. To find a synonym in Word Perfect, you must drag the curser across the word and click first on

a. Synonym.
b. Tools.
c. Thesaurus.

12. An analogy is a comparison that shows

a. a relationship.
b. a definition.
c. an example.

13. Within an analogy, a comparison that shows qualities is called an analogy of

a. classification.
b. characteristics.
c. degree.

14. The best way to expand your vocabulary is to

a. memorize every new word.
b. read frequently.
c. listen to speakers.

15. A mailing list is called a(n)

a. list serv.
b. e-mail.
c. discussion group.

The questions below (questions 16 through 20) are based on Figures 1 and 2.

FIGURE 1

Col·leen (käl′ēn, kə lēn′) [Ir.: see ff.] a feminine name
col·leen (käl′ēn, kə lēn′) *n.* [Ir. *cailin*, dim. of *caile*, girl]
[Irish] a girl
col·lege (käl′ij) *n.* [ME. & OFr. < L. *collegium*, community,
society, guild, fraternity < *collega:* see COLLEAGUE] **1.** an
association of individuals having certain powers and duties,
and engaged in some common pursuit *[*the electoral *college]*
2. [orig. with reference to the university communities of
Oxford & Cambridge] an institution of higher education
that grants degrees; university; specif., *a)* any of the
schools of a university offering instruction and granting
degrees in any of several specialized courses of study, as
liberal arts, architecture, law, medicine, etc. *b)* the
undergraduate division of a university, which offers a
general four-year course leading to the bachelor's degree
3. a school offering specialized instruction in some profession or occupation *[*a secretarial *college]* **4.** the students,
faculty, or administrators of a college **5.** a clerical group
that has been given the legal status of an ecclesiastical
corporation **6.** the building or buildings of a college
College of Cardinals the cardinals of the Roman Catholic
Church, serving as a privy council to the Pope and electing
his successor
col·le·gi·al (kə lē′jē əl) *adj.* [ME. < L. *collegialis*] **1.** with
authority or power shared equally among colleagues **2.**
same as COLLEGIATE

-Webster's New World Dictionary, 1982, p1553

FIGURE 2

unit factor   1553   unlearned

Alaska & Hawaii: 3,615,211 sq. mi.; pop. 227,000,000; cap. Washington, D.C.: also called **United States**

unit factor a gene involved in the inheritance of a given unit character

u·ni·tive (yōō′nə tiv) *adj.* [ML. *unitivus*] 1. having or characterized by unity 2. tending to unite

u·nit·ize (yōō′nə tiz′) *vt.* **-ized′, -iz′ing** [UNIT + -IZE] to make into a single unit —**u′nit·i·za′tion** *n.*

unit (magnetic) pole a magnetic pole that, when placed in a vacuum at a distance of one centimeter from an equal and like pole, will repel it with a force of one dyne

unit pricing a supplementary system of pricing commodities, esp. food items, by showing the prices in terms of standard units, as of an ounce or pint: it facilitates a comparison of prices of competing items

☆**unit rule** a rule, as in national conventions of the Democratic Party, that the entire vote of a delegation, if the State's party apparatus so chooses, shall be cast as a unit, disregarding minority votes in the delegation

u·ni·ty (yōō′nə tē) *n., pl.* **-ties** [ME. *unite* < OFr. *unité* < L. *unitas*, oneness < *unus*, ONE] 1. the state of being one, or united; oneness; singleness 2. something complete in itself; single, separate thing 3. the quality of being one in spirit, sentiment, purpose, etc.; harmony; agreement; concord; uniformity 4. *a)* unification *b)* a unified group or body 5. the quality or fact of being a totality or whole, esp. a complex that is a union of related parts 6. *a)* an arrangement of parts or material that will produce a single, harmonious design or effect in an artistic or literary production *b)* a design or effect so produced 7. constancy, continuity, or fixity of purpose, action, etc. 8. *Math. a)* any quantity, magnitude, etc. considered or identified as a unit, or 1 *b)* the numeral or unit 1 —**the (three) unities** the three principles of dramatic construction derived by French neoclassicists from Aristotle's *Poetics*, holding that a play should have one unified plot (**unity of action**), that all the action should occur within one day (**unity of time**), and that there should be one locale (**unity of place**)

SYN.—**unity** implies the oneness, as in spirit, aims, interests, feelings, etc., of that which is made up of diverse elements or individuals *[national unity]*; **union** implies the state of being united into a single organization for a common purpose *[a labor union]*; **solidarity** implies such firm and complete unity in an organization, group, class, etc. as to make for the greatest possible strength in influence, action, etc.

Univ. 1. Universalist 2. University

univ. 1. universal 2. universally 3. university

u·ni·ver·sal·ize (yōō′nə vʉr′sə līz′) *vt.* **-ized′, -iz′ing** to make universal —**u′ni·ver·sal·i·za′tion** *n.*

universal joint (or **coupling**) a joint or coupling that permits a swing of limited angle in any direction, esp. one used to transmit rotary motion from one shaft to another not in line with it, as in the drive shaft of an automobile

u·ni·ver·sal·ly (yōō′nə vʉr′s'lē) *adv.* in a universal manner; specif., *a)* in every instance *b)* in every part or place

Universal Product Code a patterned series of vertical bars of varying widths printed on packages of many consumer products: it can be read by a computerized scanner for inventory control, pricing, etc.

universal suffrage suffrage for all adult citizens

u·ni·verse (yōō′nə vʉrs′) *n.* [L. *universum*, the universe < neut. of *universus*, all together < *unus*, ONE + *versus*, pp. of *vertere*, to turn: see VERSE] 1. the totality of all the things that exist; creation; the cosmos 2. the world, or earth, as the scene of human activity 3. an area, province, or sphere, as of thought or activity, regarded as a distinct, comprehensive system —*SYN.* see EARTH

universe of discourse *Logic* the totality of facts, things, or ideas implied or assumed in a given discussion, argument, or discourse

u·ni·ver·si·ty (yōō′nə vʉr′sə tē) *n., pl.* **-ties** [ME. *universite* < MFr. *université* < ML. *universitas* < L., the whole, universe, society, guild < *universus:* see UNIVERSE] 1. an educational institution of the highest level, typically, in the U.S., with one or more undergraduate colleges, together with a program of graduate studies and a number of professional schools, and authorized to confer various degrees, as the bachelor's, master's, and doctor's 2. the grounds, buildings, etc. of a university 3. the students, faculty, or administrators of a university

u·niv·o·cal (yoo niv′ə k'l, yōō′nə vō′k'l) *adj.* having a single, sharply defined sense or nature; unambiguous

un·joint (un joint′) *vt.* 1. to separate (a joint) 2. to separate the joints of

un·just (-just′) *adj.* 1. not just or right; unfair; contrary to justice 2. [Obs.] dishonest or unfaithful

un·kempt (-kempt′) *adj.* [UN- + *kempt*, pp. of dial. *kemben*, to comb < ME. *kemben* < OE. *cemban* < *camb*, a COMB[1]] 1. not combed 2. not tidy, neat, or groomed;

UNIVERSAL JOINT

-Webster's New World Dictionary, 1982, p. 1553

16. In Figure 1, the word "college" can mean all of the following *except*

a. an association of individuals having certain powers and duties and engaged in some common pursuit.

b. electoral.

c. a school offering specialized instruction in some profession or occupation.

17. In Figure 2, the words "unit factor" and "unlearned" found at the top of the page are

a. etymologies.

b. guide words.

c. antonyms.

18. According to the dictionary entry, a synonym for the word "universe" is

a. something that exists.
b. comprehensive.
c. earth.

19. For the word "universalize," all of the following are given *except*

a. the word history.
b. the pronunciation.
c. definitions.

20. The first meaning of the word "university" is

a. the whole, universe, society, guide.
b. grounds and buildings.
c. an educational institution of the highest level.

TEST B

True-False. Read the statements below and mark whether or not the statement is true or false (T or F).

_____1. It is more important to be able to use many words than it is to recognize many words.

_____2. Technical words are words that pertain to a particular discipline.

_____3. To unlock the meaning of an unfamiliar word, you must first pronounce it correctly.

_____4. Contrast word clues suggest a relationship of similarity between two words.

_____5. To determine the exact meaning of a word with many different meanings, you must use context clues.

_____6. The root or base word is considered the main part of a word.

_____7. Stopping to look up an unknown word in the dictionary while reading is a preferred reading strategy.

_____8. Guide words in a dictionary are always at the bottom of a page.

_____9. In a dictionary, the preferred spelling of a word is usually given first.

_____10. An abridged dictionary is one which gives all definitions of a word.

_____11. The history of a word is called the schema.

_____12. Greek mythology has given us the roots for many English words.

_____13. It is not necessary to have a glossary in a textbook because words and terms needed for understanding the text are all found in a dictionary.

_____14. Words found in a glossary apply to terms within a particular field of study.

_____15. A thesaurus and a glossary may be used interchangeably.

_____16. A thesaurus may be found in Word Perfect by clicking on Tools.

_____17. Working analogies helps us in problem solving.

_____18. In an analogy, classification identifies the larger-group association.

_____19. A site where you can review topic-specific information posted by others on a particular subject is called a list serv.

_____20. After subscribing to a mailing list, you never have to worry about "unsubscribing."

CHAPTER FOUR: Main Idea

TEST A

Answer the multiple-choice questions based on the content of the chapter.

1. In most cases, the main idea is stated in

a. a phrase.
b. one complete sentence.
c. one word.

2. Which of the following words is *not* another way to express the meaning of the main idea?

a. gist
b. central focus
c. single meaning

3. The first step in finding the main idea of a reading passage is to determine

a. a general topic.
b. minor details.
c. a key word.

4. The topic describes the general category of

a. supporting details.
b. the main idea.
c. a group of key ideas.

5. Specific information that develops the main idea is composed of

a. general topics.
b. a central focus.
c. supporting details.

6. In some cases it is possible to determine the topic of a passage from

a. a key word.
b. the title of the passage.
c. the second sentence of the first paragraph.

7. When the main idea is directly stated at the beginning of a passage, the student

a. does not need to read for the details.
b. is briefed on the through-step method.
c. knows what to expect from the passage.

8. The main idea may be stated

a. anywhere in a passage.
b. at the end of a passage.
c. at the beginning of a passage.

9. Approximately what percent of college textbooks have the main idea directly stated in reading passages?

a. 30%
b. 50%
c. 75%

10. A main idea not directly stated is said to be

a. incomplete.
b. unformed.
c. implied.

TEST B

Answer the multiple-choice questions about main idea based on the content of the paragraphs below.

When they first met in 1931, Mrs. Wallis Simpson was merely one of a group of friends-fashionable, fast, and witty. She had been twice married; however, Prince Edward found her entertaining and undemanding. She appealed to his affection for things American, and it seems that her refusal to compromise and her treatment of the Prince in a manner unthinkable in an Englishwoman were additional attractions. By 1934 he had determined to marry her. It required of the Prince no effort of imagination to gauge the likely response of his family to the news; he wished to tell the King, but the opportunity never came, and in the new year the King was dead. In his first months as King, Edward grew moody, bad-tempered, and disinclined to keep appointments. In the summer of 1936 foreign papers splashed romantic photographs across their front pages. On one occasion a photograph was published which showed King Edward meeting Mrs. Simpson at a train station; it was unfortunate that on the same day he had sent his brother to perform a public duty rather than go himself, the official reason, also published, being that he was still in mourning. The British public was unwilling to accept a woman like Wallis Simpson as wife to their sovereign. For King Edward the agony was prolonged, the more so as Mrs. Simpson, seeing what she had brought about, stated her willingness to leave him. King Edward had bound himself by his word to marriage to Wallis Simpson and that meant giving up the throne. On December 10, 1936, he put his signature to the document of abdication, left for France, and married Mrs. Simpson.

-Fraser, 1975, pp. 338; 341

1. The main idea of the passage is that

a. Prince Edward gave up his throne for the love of a woman.
b. the whole of England thought Prince Edward a fool for giving up his throne.
c. King Edward was forced off the throne of England because of his relationship with an American woman.

Only a tiny percentage of the American population is healthy. More than one-third of the American population is chronically ill. And that's an understatement, because it assumes that you're ill only at the point of diagnosis of a classically defined disease. That figure doesn't take into account the idea that you can be 80 percent unwell before the first symptoms of disease manifest. It may take twenty years for enough tumor cells to show up on an X-ray or mammogram. At the time of the diagnosis, you're at the end stage of a healing crisis, not the beginning.

Another fifty million people have the early stages of disease. These are our youth. Baby boomers-forty years old and over-didn't grow up exclusively on a junk-food diet. They played outdoors and got plenty of exercise, and had junk foods a couple of times a week. Most of today's children eat junk food-or at least highly processed food-at every meal. Rather than daily physical activity, most spend the bulk of their time in sedentary pursuits, watching television or surfing the Internet. And they live in an overly excited, toxic environment. That's why their health is so much worse than those who grew up in earlier times–even as recently as the 1950s and 1960s–before fast food and microwaveable meals.

-Null, 1999, pp. 23-24

2. The first paragraph of the selection is primarily concerned with the idea that

a. only a small percentage of Americans are truly healthy.
b. baby boomers are the healthiest group in the United States.
c. fast food and microwaveable meals are healthy.

3. What is the main idea of the second paragraph of the selection?

a. In the U.S., there are fifty million people who are chronically ill.
b. Today's youth are more unhealthy than baby boomers due to unhealthy diets, toxic environments, and sedentary lifestyles.
c. In current times, the environment is so toxic that it causes most illnesses.

What makes life difficult is that the process of confronting and solving problems is a painful one. Problems, depending upon their nature, evoke in us frustration, grief, sadness, loneliness, guilt, regret, anger, fear, or despair. These are uncomfortable feelings, often as painful as any kind of physical pain. And since life poses an endless series of problems, life is always difficult. Fearing the pain involved, almost all of us, to a greater or lesser degree, attempt to avoid problems. We procrastinate, hoping that they will go away, and even take drugs to assist us in ignoring them so that by deadening ourselves to the pain, we can forget the problems that cause the pain. We attempt to skirt around problems rather than meet them head on. We attempt to get out of them rather than suffer through them. In any case, when we avoid the legitimate suffering that results from dealing with problems, we also avoid the growth that problems demand from us. Problems call forth our courage and our wisdom; indeed, they create our courage and our wisdom. It is only because of problems that we grow mentally and spiritually. As Benjamin Franklin said, "Those things that hurt, instruct." It is through the pain of confronting and resolving problems that we learn. It is in this whole process of meeting and solving problems that life has its meaning.

-Peck, 1978, pp. 16-17

4. What is the central focus of the passage?

a. Life is difficult, so you might as well resign yourself to that fact.
b. Problems evoke a range of emotions so individuals attempt to numb the pain with drugs.
c. If we are willing to confront and resolve problems, we will experience the growth needed to make life more meaningful.

Roman taste for grand architecture found expression in the bath. Initially mixed bathing was permitted, but later the sexes were segregated, with women and men bathing at different times. The baths of the Caracalla complex covered fifty acres, and approximately sixteen hundred people could be accommodated. The plan was organized along a central axis-the warm-water pool, the hot-water pool (usually circular in shape), and the cold-water pool were all located on the axis. Gymnasia flanked the pools, and gardens, barber and hairdresser shops, libraries, and meeting rooms completed the complex. Water, transported by aqueducts from outside the city and heated by fires in basements, was passed to the pools in clay or lead pipes.

Lavish marble, stucco, and painted decoration embellished the interior surfaces. By the first century A.D., the Roman statesman, Seneca, complained that new bath structures were too ornate: "We think ourselves poor if our walls are not resplendent with large and costly mirrors; if our marbles from Alexandria are not set off by mosaics, if our vaulted ceilings are not buried in glass, if our swimming pools are not lined with Thasian marble. What a vast number of statues, of columns that support nothing, but are built for decoration, merely in order to spend money!" Most Romans would not have agreed with Seneca, for they viewed the ritual of bathing and socializing within an opulent architectural environment as one of the joys of civilized life.

-Wilkins, et. al., 1994, pp. 142-143.

5. The controlling idea in paragraph one above is that

a. the three pools of the Roman bath were organized along a central axis.
b. Roman taste for grand architecture found expression in the Roman bath.
c. Romans were the first to utilize aqueducts to bring water into the city.

6. The gist of the second paragraph is that

a. though some viewed the Roman bath as too decorative and costly, the majority of Romans was appreciative of the lavish environment.
b. proprietors of Roman baths encouraged mixed bathing.
c. the baths of Caracalla included several types of Thasian marble pools.

"Violence," announced 1960s Black Power advocate H. Rap Brown, "is as American as cherry pie." At that time, his words outraged many, who not only considered them unpatriotic but also a justification of violence on the part of Brown's own group, the Black Panthers.

Several decades later, however, few will dispute that the United States is a very violent society, although when it comes to violence, this country does not have a monopoly. Violence is indeed as American as cherry pie, but also as British as boiled beef, as Russian as caviar, as Japanese as sushi. Not only is violence disturbingly widespread, but it also enjoys a very old pedigree. Thus, although it seems unlikely to be "inherently" American (or British, or Russian, or Japanese), the evidence strongly suggests that violence is "inherently" human-violence seems likely to be deeply ensconced in our biological natures.

-Barash, 2001, p. 1

7. The main thesis of the passage is that violence

a. is caused by a biologically based flaw in Americans.
b. began with the Black Panther movement.
c. is inherently human.

     The messages communicated by the eyes vary depending on the duration, direction, and quality of the eye behavior. For example, in every culture there are strict, though unstated, rules for the proper duration for eye contact. In our culture, the average length of gaze is 2.95 seconds. The average length of mutual gaze (two persons gazing at each other) is 1.18 seconds. When eye contact falls short of this amount, you may think the person is uninterested, shy, or preoccupied. When the appropriate amount of time is exceeded, you might perceive the person as showing unusually high interest. The direction of the eye also communicates. In much of the United States, you're expected to glance alternatively at the other person's face, then away, then again at the face. The rule for the public speaker is to scan the entire audience, not focusing for too long or ignoring any one area of the audience.

-DeVito, 2000, p. 132

8. What is the main idea of the paragraph?

a. Persons gazing at each other should not gaze more than 1.18 seconds.
b. Messages can be communicated by the eyes through duration, direction, and quality of the eye behavior.
c. When eye contact falls short of the expected duration, you may think the person is uninterested in you.

     Everyone in the Information-technology industry believes emphatically that there is a U.S. slow down, but no one ever admits to being touched by it. It remains a horror that happens only to other people. However, the subject is still frightening enough to monopolize the conversation at any infotech get-together.
     "We have resumes pouring in over the Internet everyday," says Ms Vandana Malaiya, Director, EximSoft of India. Nothing unusual in the software industry, except that this time, these are the professionals in the United States who are suddenly out of jobs. MNCs have been more forthcoming about their expected losses, with Nortel, GE, Motorola, Cisco, and now Compaq having announced job cuts. Others such as Sun have frozen recruitments, filling only "critical" positions.

-Phadnis, 2001

9. The best statement of the main idea is that

a. information technology in India is slowing down so the companies are recruiting from the U.S.
b. major U.S. companies announced thousands of job cuts in information technology.
c. unemployed U.S. information-technology professionals are seeking employment in India due to a U S. slow down.

In the broadest sense, anything that promotes your business might be considered advertising. Newspapers are an inexpensive way to reach a mass audience. They are flexible and good for price advertising. Magazines offer a slightly better opportunity to catch a reader's attention than newspapers do, but they typically cost more. Magazines are good for promoting your company's image and building its credibility. Radio is a relatively low-cost, high-impact choice for local advertising. It is one of the best ways to reach a targeted market, but costs are slightly higher than for print ads. Repetition is especially important in radio advertising. Television advertising is extremely high-impact, but it is expensive to buy spots on major networks. Cable channels that will air your ad in select markets are more affordable. Yellow Pages advertising is not cheap, but it delivers hot prospects-people who are ready to buy. It is a good choice for local and area-specific businesses.

-"Advertising Basics," 2001

10. The passage is primarily concerned with

a. several types of advertising, each with its own advantages.
b. anything that might promote your business.
c. the advantages of television advertising.

CHAPTER FIVE: Supporting Details and Organizational Patterns

TEST A

Answer the multiple-choice questions based on the content of the chapter.

1. One way to organize details and recognize levels of importance is to

a. re-read the material.
b. list main ideas.
c. make an outline.

2. All details

a. should be memorized.
b. carry only minor significance.
c. develop the main idea.

3. Details that are included just to make a passage more interesting

a. are considered minor details.
b. are considered major details.
c. have the same level of importance as the main idea.

4. Major details

a. "fill out" a passage.
b. directly support the main idea.
c. are only stated indirectly.

5. A transitional phrase/word that signals a minor detail, which shows secondary support, would be

a. "next."
b. "first."
c. "for instance."

6. When reading detailed directions, a reader should

a. pay attention to each detail.
b. memorize the major and minor details.
c. try to get the gist of the directions and ignore any step-by-step instructions.

7. Patterns of organization

a. occur only in passages about history.
b. are blueprints for organizing your thinking.
c. do not facilitate notetaking.

8. Key words that signal contrast in a passage include all of the following *except*

a. "like."
b. "however."
c. "on the contrary."

9. In simple listing, the order of the list is

a. relevant.
b. somewhat crucial.
c. of no importance.

10. As an organizational pattern, classification is used to

a. simplify a complex topic.
b. determine universal concepts.
c. define an idea.

11. To help you visualize the meaning of new terminology from a textbook chapter, it is best to

a. first learn all the basic vocabulary.
b. re-read the paragraphs in which the terms appear.
c. write down examples.

12. A simple list of details signals an organizational pattern of

a. definition.
b. description.
c. narration.

13. The writing of history is usually organized through which of the following patterns of organization?

a. classification or definition
b. description or sequence
c. time order or narration

14. A transitional word/phrase that does not indicate time order is

a. "December 21, 1951."
b. "afterward."
c. "for example."

15. One effective way to recognize the organizational pattern of comparison/contrast is to look for

a. time-order words.
b. similarities and differences in the topics.
c. a simple list of details.

16. Words such as "thus," "consequently," "so," and/or "as a result of" all signal the organizational pattern of

a. cause and effect.
b. definition.
c. classification.

17. Transition words alert the reader

a. to anticipate a pattern of organization.
b. to review the previous paragraph only.
c. that the writer is continuing or changing his/her thoughts.

For questions 18 through 20, choose the appropriate transition word or phrase to fill in the blanks within the paragraphs below.

Rainwater from melting snow that would otherwise be lost can be captured by dams on rivers and stored in large reservoirs behind the dams. This increases the annual supply by collecting fresh surface water during wet periods and storing it for use during dry periods.
_____, dams control the flow of rivers and can reduce the danger of flooding in areas below the dam, provide a controllable supply of water for irrigating land below the dam, and generate relatively cheap electricity for local and regional residents.

- Miller, 1988, pp. 168-169

18. The most appropriate transition word/phrase for the blank above is

a. "in addition."
b. "for example."
c. "first."

Faulty construction, earthquakes, sabotage, or war can cause dams to fail, taking a terrible toll in lives and property. _____, in 1972 a dam failure in Buffalo Creek, West Virginia, killed 125 people, and another in Rapid City, South Dakota, killed 237 and caused more than $1 billion in damages. According to a 1986 study by the Federal Emergency Management Agency, the United States has 1,900 unsafe dams in populated areas.

-Miller, 1988, p. 169

19. The most appropriate transition word/phrase for the blank above is

a. "finally."
b. "while."
c. "for example."

One solution to water supply problems is heavier reliance on groundwater, which makes up about 95% of the world's supply of fresh water. However, the increased use of groundwater gives rise to several problems: First, aquifer depletion or overdraft when groundwater is withdrawn faster than it is recharged by precipitation; second, subsidence, or sinking of the ground as groundwater is withdrawn; third, salt-water intrusion into freshwater aquifers in coastal areas; and _____, groundwater contamination from human activities.

-Miller, 1988, p. 171

20. The most appropriate transition word/phrase for the blank above is

a. "whereas."
b. "lastly."
c. "consequently."

TEST B

After reading the paragraph, decide what pattern of organization the writer is utilizing. Then choose the correct option for the multiple-choice question.

The rise of agriculture-based urban societies created an environmental impact far exceeding that of hunting-and-gathering societies. Forests were cut down and grasslands were plowed up to provide vast areas of crop land and grazing land to feed the growing populations of these emerging civilizations and to provide wood for fuel and for buildings. Such massive land clearing destroyed and altered the habitats of many forms of plant and animal wildlife, endangering their existence and in some cases causing or hastening their extinction.

-Miller, 1988, p. 18

1. The pattern of organization the writer employs is

a. comparison.
b. summary.
c. cause-effect.

Although the steps to becoming a police officer vary with each jurisdiction, the criterion for selection generally includes a series of steps: First, larger police departments, as well as state police agencies, may use four kinds of written tests. Smaller departments will usually administer some form of intelligence test, as well as a psychological screening test. The next stage usually is to determine whether a candidate has the physical agility necessary to be a police officer. Third, many departments conduct oral interviews to test the candidate's ability to evaluate and reason through several difficult situations. Some advanced testing may include an interactive training video or role playing, where the applicant is asked at different stages to provide a solution. Ethical questions are always included in the examination. Last, departments continue to ask applicants about their previous drug use, a question that is repeated during the polygraph examination. If the use of drugs other than marijuana is found to be more than experimental in the last three to five years, applicants are likely to be eliminated.

-Bartollas and Hahn, 1999, pp. 55-56

2. The author makes her/his point through the use of

a. sequence.
b. example.
c. location.

The British Medical Association (BMA) is a professional organization for doctors in Great Britain. It exists primarily to provide technical and professional information to member doctors and to protect the standards and practices of the medical profession on matters of education, training, qualifications to practice, and discipline in instances of malpractice. The BMA is a good example of an effective associational interest group because, in protecting the professional and financial interest of its members, its professional staff and members take many actions to influence the policies of the British government regarding the health care system. The BMA is concerned about public policies regarding such issues as advertising by professionals, judicial rulings on liability, personal and business taxation policies, certification of health care paraprofessionals, support for medical research, and so on.

-Danziger, 1998, p. 66

3. The overall organizational pattern used by the writer is

a. cause-effect.
b. definition.
c. classification.

Most of the early conservationists, because they were intellectuals whose writing did not reach popular audiences, had relatively little influence on politicians. For instance, between 1830 and 1870, a number of early conservationists such as George Catlin, Horace Greeley, Ralph Waldo Emerson, and Henry David Thoreau warned that America's timber and grassland resources were being exploited at an alarming rate through overgrazing, deforestation, and general misuse. They proposed that part of the land be withdrawn from public use and preserved in the form of national parks, but their words generally went unheeded.

-Miller, 1988, p. 20

4. Which of the following organizational patterns does the author use to get the point across to the reader?

a. contrast
b. example
c. location

Let us return to the topic of birthing magic, and consider two examples, one from Panama and one from Malaysia. In both, midwives and shamans help the mother in moving the baby down the birth canal and out into the world. But they do so by drawing on very different sets of images and values. Cuna society, in Panama, holds high the culture of heroes and battles. There, a shaman, someone who can be possessed by good spirits, sings to help childbirth. In his song the shaman describes in painstaking detail the events leading up to his own arrival at the woman's houses, the woman experiencing pain, the midwife coming to call him, and then the journey of the friendly spirits.

Now contrast the chants recited by a healer in a Malay village studied by Carol Laderman. As in the Cuna case, the ritual specialist only intervenes when the midwife can no longer cope with the difficult birth. The specialist, called a "bomoh," recites a story about God's creation of the world and of the first couple, and then about the creation of the individual human. Even if the woman does not hear every detail of the story, women are, says Laderman, soothed by its familiar references.

-Bowen, 1998, pp. 71-72

5. The pattern of organization used by the author is

a. description.
b. sequence.
c. compare/contrast.

        Outside in the reception hall, she tried to remember how to get back to the courtyard. Her head was pounding. She had not known that Lady Alais had borrowed from the bishop. That was foolish. Heloise turned down a passageway and saw a sullen sky ahead. When she realized that the passage opened into the cloister, she wheeled and hastily retraced her steps. Stalking toward her was a tall monk surrounded by a cluster of chattering novices. Something about the set of his shoulders made her tense up. A smile began to form at the corners of her mouth. Abelard's eyes met hers and slid past the side of her head. Suddenly he was behind her.
        The stone walls heaved around her. Blindly, she lifted one foot and then the other, not caring where they took her. He had pretended not to know her; he had looked at her as if she were a stranger. She walked on until she came out into the yard. The cobbles, slippery from the rain, made her stumble. The cathedral bells began to roar.

-Meade, 1979, p. 229

6. The organizational patterns utilized in the passage above are

a. narration and description.
b. description and sequence.
c. location and cause-effect.

        In Japan, new forms of healing and worship bring trance mechanisms together with the Japanese cultural heritage to heal patients suffering from what we would call psychosomatic illnesses. The New Religions developed in response to modern life situations, and particularly, in response to the new illnesses and anxieties felt by many newly urban Japanese. Those millions of Japanese who have moved into cities since the 1950s have found themselves cut off from their accustomed places for ritual practice and sources of religious strength. They also found themselves living in a radically new era, with new kinds of pressures on the job and at home.
        Let us take a look at one of the new religions, that of Mahikari. Mahikari, meaning "True Light," was founded in 1959 when a man of lower-class origins in Tokyo recovered from illness and debt and received a revelation from God that he was to change his name and bring light and health to the people of Japan. This man, now known as Okada Kotama, began to heal people through the use of amulets. His sect grew rapidly in popularity-by the late 1970s Mahikari had

over 150 *dojos* (buildings for practicing spiritual disciplines) and somewhere between 50,000 and 100,000 active members.

-Bowen, 1998, p. 76

7. Which of the following organizational patterns does the author use?

a. example
b. definition
c. summary

His face took her breath away; it was not only that he was extremely handsome-she had seen beautiful men-it was a face made to be adored. Now she could understand why Jourdain, why all these young men in the garden today, worshiped the man; he dazzled like the noonday sun. The magnificent grin, the hypnotic intelligence of the blue eyes, the mouth so elegant and mobile, they shouted to every passerby, "Love me, admire me, possess me if you can!" Unable to face him any longer she looked away and said coldly, "I suppose you're accustomed to these mob scenes whenever you lecture."

-Meade, 1979, p. 229

8. The pattern of organization used in the above paragraph is

a. definition.
b. description.
c. classification.

In many circles, American culture today revolves around thinness and beauty. Simple evidence of this fact is that everyone knows at least one person who is on a diet. But how can we tell what is normal dieting behavior versus a problem which can become life-threatening? And how can we identify these life-threatening behaviors before it is too late? Certainly we can identify *anorexia nervosa* after a sufferer has lost too much weight. But where is the line that separates dieting from a serious illness? To answer these questions, scholars of psychological studies have determined typical behaviors of people suffering from an eating disorder. (Unfortunately the findings are complicated by the difficulty in diagnosing a person when he or she is in the beginning stages of the disease.) However, these early warning signs should help you to determine if you or a loved one is on a destructive eating disorder path: exhibiting low self-esteem, feeling of a lack of control over life, having a distorted body image, obsessing on over-achievement, surceasing the menstrual cycle (females), thinking constantly of food, isolating self from friends and family (including dining alone), feeling fatigue, growing more facial and body hair and losing scalp hair.

-Goldberg, 2001

9. The pattern of organization used by the author is

a. location.
b. sequence.
c. simple listing.

      In conclusion, cultural patterns are clearly very influential regarding the expression of both male and female aggression. Cross-culturally men tend to engage in more physical aggression than women. There is tentative evidence, however, from several cultural settings that women may make greater use of indirect aggression than men. In addition, some cultures have very low levels of physical aggression overall, among both sexes.

-Barash, 2001, p. 185

10. What is the organizational pattern utilized by the author?

a. definition
b. description
c. summary

CHAPTER SIX: Textbook Learning

TEST A

True-False. Read the statements below and mark whether or not the statement is true or false (T or F).

_____1. Annotating is a study system in which the student underlines and highlights the text.

_____2. The best strategy for marking your text to remember material is to mark as much as possible.

_____3. The best way to annotate is to read the entire chapter first, then go back to annotate.

_____4. Notetaking is useful for textbook study as well as for class lectures.

_____5. The Cornell Method of notetaking involves writing down main ideas and supporting details.

_____6. A summary is a simple listing of supporting details.

_____7. One advantage of writing a summary is that it can provide you with reference notes for later study.

_____8. When writing a summary, be sure to copy sentences directly from the source.

_____9. When citing an author directly, you must place his/her words within quotation marks.

_____10. Always begin your summary with a striking detail to catch the reader's attention.

_____11. One advantage of outlining is that it aids you in organizing your thoughts for essay writing.

_____12. In an outline, letters, numbers, and indentations designate "fillers."

_____13. Mapping helps to stimulate prior knowledge.

_____14. Mapping is a study strategy which gives a visual display of what was read.

_____15. It is a good idea to find a study buddy so that you can copy his/her work.

____ 16. An analogy shows a similarity in some respect between things that are otherwise dissimilar.

_____17. The only reliable encyclopedia for preliminary research is the *Encyclopedia Brittanica*.

_____18. The term "periodical literature" includes magazines.

_____19. Articles in scholarly journals are written by generalists-not specialists in the field.

_____20. An abstract is a brief summary that describes the purpose and findings of an article.

TEST B

You are to read the selection below on the Enneagram, a psychological system which is primarily concerned with personality types. Then, choose a task to complete from Option A, Option B, or Option C. OPTION A: Write a brief summary of the article. OPTION B: Outline the article. OPTION C: Map the article above in a way other than the nine-pointed circle, including the main characteristics of each type. Be as creative as you like.

The word *ennea* is Greek for "nine," and the Enneagram is a nine-pointed figure that has its roots in Pythagorean theory (see Figure 1). It reveals to individuals information about unconscious patterns, habitual preoccupations, underlying fears, and misused strengths. What sets the Enneagram apart from other personality systems is that it contains such detailed, useful information about what drives us to behave as we do. It's valuable not just for those seeking to understand themselves but also as a source of insight into one's friends and family, colleagues, and even enemies.

The Enneagram was first adapted to understanding personality types by a Bolivian psychiatrist names Oscar Ichazo in the early 1950s. As David Daniels, psychiatrist, states it: "Embedded in each type is our basic belief about the world and how we live in it. In addition, the Enneagram shows us the aspect of our underlying essence and the corresponding path of healing. If you are fully developed, you can incorporate all nine types rather than skewing toward just one."

Through realizing the type that we are, the Enneagram exposes our fixations–fixations which drive our personalities. For example, being a Six an individual's fixations are fear and doubt. Recognizing this, the individual can open the door to healthier states of mind (such as, courage and faith, the "higher opposites"). "The work of the type is to stop being that type," says Ichazo. "The fixation is dissolved by obtaining an understanding of the other eight positions."

-Schwartz, 1995

FIGURE 1

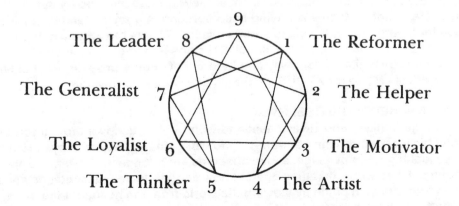

THE ENNEAGRAM   -Riso, 1990, p. 24

The following types are adapted from Helen Palmer's book, *The Enneagram,* and James Wall's article, "By the numbers."

POINT ONE: "THE REFORMER/THE PERFECTIONIST"
When young, Ones learned to monitor themselves to avoid making mistakes; they had to be correct in the eyes of others, and earned love by being perfect. They worry about getting it right; focuses on "should" and "must." For this reason, they tend to deny themselves pleasure. They are usually driven by anger, but deny it or are not consciously aware of it; Ones are disappointed in on others who make mistakes. Motivated by anger which is internalized, they express it by constantly criticizing and correcting the imperfections in others. Ones do, however, truly appreciate a job well done. Ask a POINT ONE to give a one-word description of him/herself and s/he will like say that s/he is "hard-working and that life is difficult."

POINT TWO: "THE HELPER/THE GIVER"
Twos have a marked need to be liked and earn love by being helpful. When young, they learned that survival depends on others' approval, so relationships weigh heavily in their lives. Twos need affection and avoid rejection at all costs. They manage others' lives, support and please intimates. They adapt their feelings to suit others which ensures them of popularity. On the dark side, this giving is geared to getting something in return. They feel good being the assistant. Motivated by anxiety and responds to the "heart" as opposed to the "head" or the instinctive "gut." What does a POINT TWO feel about him/herself? "I am helpful."

POINT THREE: "THE MOTIVATOR/THE PERFORMER"
When young, Threes were given accolades because of their achievements; instead of asking how they felt about their day, Threes were asked how well they had done that day. This is the success category. Threes earn love through achievement and image, and they become extremely depressed when facing a loss. They believe that status guarantees love. Therefore, work is all, and Threes find retirement especially difficult. Says "I am what I do." Persona becomes reality. Driven by a deep sense of anxiety to avoid failure, Threes handle anxiety by denying its presence. Men in this category like to be thought of as totally masculine; women like to be seen as completely feminine. A THREE'S motto is "I am what I do."

POINT FOUR: "THE ARTIST"/"THE ROMANTIC
The underlying theme of childhood for a Four is loss; they were abandoned by someone important early in life. Another theme is having been born into a grieving family, in which the child was valued for identifying with a close adult's misery. This is the artistic category, and the Four looks for love at a distance. Fours feel special, the possessor of special talent. They usually long for what is unavailable, far away and hard to get. Fours possess a sensitivity to others in pain and crisis. Motto for a FOUR: "Others have what I am missing."

POINT FIVE: "THE THINKER"/"THE OBSERVER"
This is the scholar, the thinker, who always needs to withdraw to discover more information. Fives like a protected work environment, preferring to work alone. They employ carefully planned agendas. Always looking for knowledge, a Five observes life but doesn't commit to spiritual or intimate connection. Fives worry that they do not know enough to gain acceptance and love from others. Removed from the pain of life by viewing the world from the head, not the heart, the POINT FIVE"S motto is: "I am knowing."

POINT SIX: "THE LOYALIST"/"THE TROOPER"

During childhood and adolescence, Sixes lost faith in authority–they remember being at a loss when needing to act on their own behalf because an authority figures loomed overhead. Sixes generally are rebellious by nature. Mistrusting authority, Sixes are insecure and need reassurance constantly. They often end up in middle management and identifies with the underdog. Constantly on the look out for causes and protectors to whom they can be loyal. Ask a POINT SIX about him/herself, and the answer might be "I am loyal when the cause is right."

POINT SEVEN: "THE GENERALIST"/"THE EPICURE

When faced with fear, Sevens look not at all concerned. They move toward people in an attempt to charm and disarm with pleasantry. Early in life, Sevens were faced with a frightening occurrence. Therefore, they diffuse their fear by escaping into the limitless possibilities of imagination. Sevens enjoy the initial attraction in love, and are drawn to pleasure. Always looking for new adventures, Sevens are often fearful of commitment to a single course of action. To avoid deep or painful feelings, they talk, plan and intellectualize. Talking his or her way out of trouble, a POINT SEVEN'S motto is. "I am nice."

POINT EIGHT: "THE LEADER"/"THE BOSS

This is the champion. Young Eights find themselves in combative situations where the strong are respected and the weak are not. Hence, Eights find love through protection and power. They gravitate to positions of authority and control. Eights tend to deny dependency and avoid softer emotions. They know they have the truth and don't want to hear what others have to say. The world is an all-or-nothing arena; there is no middle ground. Rather than being cowed by conflict, Eights find their identity as enforcers of justice--people are either fair or unfair. A POINT EIGHT'S motto? "I am powerful."

POINT NINE: "THE PEACEMAKER"/"THE MEDIATOR

As children, Nines felt overlooked and consequently formed the habit of discounting their own essential needs. Common to Nines is the feeling of not being heard when voicing an opinion. In addition, Nines realized that showing anger directly did not help. So, Nines are negotiators, always trying to keep the peace. Nines are excellent fence-sitters. By adopting many points of view, they avoid commitment to any one of them. Procrastination is a purposeful habit. Recognizes what is important in others' lives, but has difficulty forming personal position. What would a POINT NINE say? "Don't worry about me; I am okay."

Palmer believes that people are attracted to this modeling method in part because the Enneagram links personality type to specific aspects of what she terms the human essence, rather than to the accidental elements of personality. Though everyone shares characteristics of all nine types, the principle of the system is that one type dominates in each of us, shaping how we view the world and how we relate to others. The value of identifying ourselves on the circle is that once we know ourselves, we are on the road to rising above our limitations. Further, once we recognize the type occupied by others, we might find that it becomes easier to accept others for what they are.

-Wall, 1996, pp. 739-740

MASTERY TEST I

TEST A

This test covers terms that were used in Chapter One through Chapter Six. Match the term on the left with its appropriate definition on the right. Write the corresponding letter in the space provided.

_____1. abstract

_____2. analogy

_____3. annotating

_____4. cause and effect

_____5. root

_____6. main idea

_____7. Web pages

_____8. contrast

_____9. Cornell System

_____10. definition

_____11. details

_____12. hypertext links

_____13. etymology

_____14. mnemonics

_____15. periodical

_____16. inference

a. meaning that is not directly stated but suggested through clues

b. electronic system of more than 25,000 computer networks using a common language, connecting millions of users around the world

c. system of notetaking

d. short paragraph that summarizes an article

e. central message that the author is trying to convey

f. techniques to help your brain organize and recall information by using mental "tricks"

g. first stage of reading

h. stem of a word derived primarily from Latin and Greek

I. a "computer chip" in your brain

j. a short, informal business note

k. sites of information on the Internet

l. comparison that measures your word knowledge and ability to see relationships

m. specifics in a passage that support the main idea

n. study of word origins

o. organizational pattern listing differences between items

p. method of highlighting main ideas, significant details, and key terms using a system of notations

q. pattern of paragraph organization showing elements as causing a result

r. in Web technology, phrases that appear as bold blue text

s. at this level you may answer detail questions asking *who, what, when,* and *where*

t. publication that comes out on a regular schedule

u. pattern of organization randomly listing items in a series

(continued on next page)

_____17. Internet

_____18. interpretive

_____19. previewing

_____20. literal level

_____21. schema

_____22. transitions

_____23. simple listing

_____24. memo

_____25. minutes

v. at this level you make assumptions and draw conclusions based on the facts and clues in the passage

w. pattern of organization initially defining a concept and expanding with examples and restatements

x. signal words

y. the official record of a business meeting

TEST B

Read the following selection, then answer the multiple-choice and True-False questions based on the content of the passage. Utilize the concepts and skills you have learned in any way that you feel will aid in your comprehension of the material.

Once, at the height of the Korean War, I found myself unavoidably eavesdropping on an encounter in a Tokyo commuter train between a Japanese girl who erroneously assumed that she knew how to speak English and a young American lieutenant whose Japanese consisted of half a dozen mispronounced phrases that had made their way into G.I. Slang. Because the girl had initiated the conversation, the American had jumped to the conclusion that she was sexually available and was politely but insistently trying to convey his readiness to strike a bargain. Meantime, the girl, who was actually a touchingly naive coed from a local university, was eagerly seeking to explain how much she and some of her fellow political science majors would welcome a chance to engage the lieutenant in a discussion of the foreign policies of the Truman administration.

As it happened, I was obliged to get off the train before this dialogue reached what must have been a mutually frustrating <u>denouement</u>. But it has stuck in my mind ever since as a microcosmic example of a problem which in its ultimate implications is neither funny nor trivial. Complex as the social interaction is between Japanese themselves, the interaction between Japanese and foreigners is trickier still. And not infrequently the consequences of such encounters are both unexpected and disappointing-chiefly because Japanese and non-Japanese so often approach each other with radically different assumptions and some serious mutual misperceptions.

-Christopher, p. 170

1. The main idea of the passage is that

a. during the time of the Korean War, many American G.I.s married Japanese women.
b. because Japanese and non-Japanese often approach each other with different assumptions, it is difficult to communicate.
c. the man who was eavesdropping had a right to criticize the American G.I. and the Japanese girl.

2. According to the passage, the Japanese girl

a. was attending a local university.
b. had studied English for many years.
c. was reluctant to speak to the foreigner.

3. <u>Denouement</u>, as used in paragraph two, most nearly means

a. beginning.
b. train ride.
c. ending.

4. According to the passage, who initiated the conversation?

a. the narrator
b. the G.I.
c. the Japanese girl

5. As used in the passage, the word <u>convey</u> means to

a. deny.
b. insist.
c. relate.

_____6. The man got off the train before the Japanese girl.

_____7. Truman was president of the U.S. during World War II.

_____8. The young girl wanted to meet with the G.I. again to discuss foreign policy.

_____9. The conversation between the American G.I. and the Japanese girl made an impression on the eavesdropper.

_____10. According to the narrator, social interaction between Japanese is difficult.

TEST C

Read the selection below on economic growth and achievement motivation. Then, answer the questions which follow.

That the economic fortunes of nations rise and fall over time is obvious. In the late 1950s, graphs indicated that the United States was truly the dominant economic power in the world: it accounted for a majority of the world's output of steel, automobiles, and electricity, to name just a few important items. Today, of course, such graphs tell a very different story. The United States no longer accounts for most of the world production in these areas; and in recent years, the U.S. rate of growth has been exceeded by that in several Asian countries. What factors contribute to such trends? Most persons, including economists, would list such factors as the price and availability of natural resources, labor costs, and government policies that encourage growth. To this list, psychologists would add another factor: national differences in achievement motivation.

While achievement motivation is certainly an individual process, some evidence points to the conclusion that average levels of this motive vary sharply across cultures. For example, in classic research on this topic, McClelland (1985) analyzed stories told to children in twenty-two different cultures. McClelland analyzed the stories with respect to the degree to which they showed themes of achievement motivation. The major finding was clear: achievement motivation scores were highly <u>correlated</u> <u>with</u> economic growth. In other words, the greater the emphasis placed on achievement in the stories told to children in various nations, the more rapid the economic growth in these nations as the children grew up.

While these results may seem surprising, they have been confirmed repeatedly. For example, in a <u>massive</u> study involving more than 12,000 participants in forty-one different countries, Furnham, Kirkcaldy, and Lynn (1994) examined the relationship between a wide range of attitudes closely related to achievement motivation, and two indicators of economic growth: 1) the amount of income produced by a country; and 2) percentage of increase in economic output from year to year. Results showed a significant relationship between achievement-related attitudes and economic growth. For instance, across all countries studied, attitudes toward competitiveness were a significant predictor of economic growth: The stronger the competitiveness, the greater the rate of growth.

Of course, such research does not show that differences in achievement motivation across various cultures *cause* differences in economic growth; however, the fact that achievement motivation does influence individual performance suggests that investigating cultural differences in this motive may indeed provide us with insights into why certain countries suddenly rise to economic prominence at particular times in their history.

-Baron, pp. 361-362

1. The writer supports the main idea through the use of

a. analogies.
b. statistical studies.
c. examples.

2. In McClelland's study, how many different cultures were analyzed?

a. twenty-two
b. forty-one
c. 12,000

3. The phrase correlated with, as used in the passage, most nearly means

a. negated by.
b. related to.
c. in opposition to.

4. The results of the studies on achievement motivation seem surprising because

a. they have been confirmed repeatedly.
b. most individuals know that economic growth is solely dependent on the availability of natural resources.
c. it is uncommon to relate economic growth to achievement motivation.

5. This passage was most probably written by a(n)

a. psychologist interested in reasons for economic growth.
b. Asian economist interested in psychology.
c. administrator of the steel industry.

6. Massive, as used in paragraph three, most nearly means

a. overwhelming.
b. huge.
c. bulky.

7. Furnham, Kirkaldy, and Lynn's study (1994) emphasized

a. labor costs and government policies that encourage economic growth.
b. children's stories.
c. competitiveness.

8. The major finding of the 1994 study was that

a. attitudes toward competitiveness were a significant predictor of economic growth.
b. the greater the emphasis placed on achievement in children's stories, the more rapid the economic growth in those nations as the children grew up.
c. national differences in achievement motivation are not significant.

9. The main idea of this passage is that

a. the United States is no longer the dominant economic power, and therefore needs to be more competitive.
b. the economic fortunes of nations are influenced by the factor of achievement motivation, and investigating cultural differences in this motive may provide us with important information.
c. results of achievement motivation studies are surprising.

10. The last paragraph suggests that achievement motivation

a. causes economic growth.
b. has no effect on economic growth.
c. may not cause but may influence economic growth.

CHAPTER SEVEN: Test-Taking Strategies

Answer the multiple-choice questions based on the content of the chapter.

TEST A

1. High test scores should reflect your

a. ability to cram the night before the test.
b. use of test-taking gimmicks.
c. knowledge and ability.

2. Standardized tests measure

a. content-based material.
b. mastery of skills developed over a period of time.
c. knowledge of test-taking tricks.

3. Test preparation enhances

a. self-confidence.
b. speed reading.
c. anxiety.

4. If you are not sure of an answer, you should

a. skip it because "omits" will not count against you.
b. mark the question number and return to it later.
c. guess and move on to another question to save time.

5. After your test is returned, you should review it

a. because the instructor suggested it.
b. to challenge the grade.
c. to learn from your errors.

6. Of the following, which question type have you not yet studied?

a. author's tone
b. organizational patterns
c. inference

7. It is better not to read test questions first because

a. it takes too much of the allotted time.
b. you will have too many purposes for reading.
c. you will pay too much attention to the main idea.

8. Read the first sentence of the test passage carefully because it

a. sets the stage for what is to come.
b. is always the most difficult.
c. usually states important supporting details.

9. Main Idea questions are designated by such words or phrases as

a. "suggests"/"implies."
b. "it is stated"/"the author asserts."
c. "primarily concerned with"/"central focus."

10. The best strategy for finding the answer to a detail question is to

a. re-read the first sentence and determine the topic.
b. find a key word in the question options and then the same word in the passage.
c. skim the passage to understand the gist of the passage.

11. "Drawing a conclusion" is categorized as what type of question?

a. implied meaning
b. detail
c. stated main idea

12. In an opinion passage, the author's purpose is usually to

a. describe.
b. persuade.
c. define.

13. The purpose of fiction passages is usually to

a. objectify.
b. narrate.
c. explain.

14. To answer vocabulary in context, a student should

a. break down the word into parts and try to recognize the root.
b. re-read the passage to be certain s/he covered all the context.
c. re-read the sentences before and after the word, and the sentence the word is in.

15. In taking multiple-choice tests, a student should

a. read no further (to save time) if the first option is correct.
b. read all the options no matter what.
c. skim the options, then re-read the passage.

16. "One hundred percent" words

a. qualify.
b. are absolute.
c. are indefinite.

17. On a true-false test, "100 percent" words would not include

a. "almost"/"nearly"/"about."
b. "only"/"none"/"must."
c. "always"/"forever"/"no one."

18. Adding an incorrect "and," "but," or "because" phrase to a true statement makes it

a. partially true, therefore true.
b. true.
c. false.

19. If two test-question options are synonymous

a. choose the more important one.
b. bring this to the instructor's attention.
c. eliminate both.

20. A student can simplify an essay question by

a. dividing it into parts.
b. asking another student for clarification.
c. writing a brief summary of the material before writing the essay.

TEST B

The multiple-choice questions below are based on the discussion regarding question types in the chapter. Look at the question stems below, then choose the type of question indicated by the stem.

1. It is stated in the passage that . . .

a. implied meaning
b. detail
c. purpose

2. The central theme of the selection is . . .

a. vocabulary
b. implied meaning
c. main idea

3. The word *pheromone* most nearly means. . .

a. purpose
b. detail
c. vocabulary

4. All of the following are true *except* . . .

a. detail
b. purpose
c. implied meaning

5. The primary focus of the first paragraph is . . .

a. detail
b. main idea
c. purpose

6. It is suggested by the author that . . .

a. purpose
b. main idea
c. implied meaning

7. The author's primary aim in the passage is to . . .

a. purpose
b. main idea
c. vocabulary

8. As used in the second paragraph, the best definition of *euphoria* is. . .

a. detail
b. vocabulary
c. purpose

9. The reader can conclude from the passage that . . .

a. main idea
b. implied meaning
c. purpose

10. The best title for this passage is . . .

a. purpose
b. detail
c. main idea

TEST C

Applying the tips for test-taking explained in the chapter, answer the following true-false and multiple-choice questions which are based on the content of the chapter. Write the specific tip that you used to answer the question.

_____1. A student can always pass a test by using test-taking strategies.

TIP:

_____2. On teacher-made tests, the number of points for each item will sometimes vary.

TIP:

_____3. Time is usually a major consideration on a test, but you really don't need to wear a watch.

TIP:

_____4. Test questions are not unpredictable.

TIP:

_____5. Writing the answer to an essay question involves all of the following *except*

  a. brainstorming and numbering your ideas.
  b. repeating the topic over and over again.
  c. organizing and planning your ideas.

TIP:

_____6. The primary purpose of lesson seven is to

    a. narrate.
    b. relate a story.
    c. inform.

TIP:

_____7. To improve your grades on an essay test, it is a good idea to read an

    a. "A" paper.
    b. related research article.
    c. grammar text.

TIP:

_____8. A major consideration on tests is

    a. the number of sections.
    b. the number of pages.
    c. time.

TIP:

_____9. Mnemonics are

    a. strategies for writing essays.
    b. techniques to help your recall information.
    c. types of viruses.

TIP:

_____10. For an essay exam, a student should use a formal style

    a. because a college professor, not your friend, will be reading your answer.
    b. to show their professor respect.
    c. because it is easier.

CHAPTER EIGHT: Efficient Reading

Answer the multiple-choice questions based on the content of the chapter.

TEST A

1. For college students, the average reading rate with 70% comprehension is

a. 250 words per minute.
b. 1,000 words per minute.
c. 300 words per minute.

2. If you are reading below the average rate of an adult reader, you

a. may need glasses.
b. might have trouble completing assignments.
c. will probably do well on standardized tests.

3. An increase in reading speed usually means

a. an improvement in comprehension.
b. poorer comprehension.
c. slower eye movements.

4. According to Pinette, to fully concentrate a student needs

a. more challenging material.
b. good health and rest.
c. external and internal distractions.

5. An example of an external distraction would be

a. worrying about money.
b. visualizing during the reading process.
c. a telephone call.

6. **Regression is**

a. backtracking.
b. speed reading.
c. a technique for improving concentration.

7. **Subvocalization is**

a. moving your lips as you read.
b. hearing the words in your mind as you read.
c. pronouncing out loud as you read.

8. **Reading speed can be increased by**

a. vocalizing.
b. decreasing the number of fixations.
c. reading word for word.

9. **According to the author, an effective speed-reading technique is**

a. underlining details.
b. to read passively.
c. using a pen as a pacer.

10. **Reading a selection on economics should take**

a. more time than reading a popular magazine article.
b. less time than reading a popular magazine article.
c. the same amount of time as reading a popular magazine article.

TEST B: TIMED READING

A. Tear out this page to use for a skimming quiz. You will be skimming a page from a telephone book which can be found on the next page (using the information you learned in this chapter about eye movement techniques). Write your answers in the spaces provided below. You will have 2 MINUTES and 30 SECONDS to answer the questions. Your teacher will tell you when to begin and when to put your pencil down.

1. From what town's telephone book is this listing taken?   1._____

2. Is Clayton C. Barnard's address listed?   2._____

3. How many entries for Brown are there?   3._____

4. What is the number of Buddy's Service Station?   4._____

5. What is Kirby Archambeault's middle initial?   5._____

6. What is W. L. Brown's nickname?   6._____

7. What is Mrs. Cordeal Carter's number?   7._____

8. How many religious organizations are listed?   8._____

9. There is one reverend listed. What is his name?   9._____

10. What is Melanie Campione's P. O. Box number?

          10._____

COBBTOWN

INSTRUCTIONS

Calls from COBBTOWN to METTER and COLLINS, and from METTER and COLLINS to COBBTOWN, dial the number as listed in the directory.

FOR REPAIR SERVICE CALL 685-2124

A

A & P BUILDERS Cobbtown	684-2904
Abarca Eutiquito	684-2855
Alberson E E Rt 1	684-3335
Aldrich Tina	684-2317
Alexander John Rt 1	684-5508
Alfaro Daniel & Felicitas Rt 2 Bx 309	684-2338
Allen G W (Bud)	684-2440
Anderson Bob P Rt 2	684-4584
Anderson Charlie Rt 1 Clns	684-4143
Anderson Heather	684-2586
Anderson J Rt 2	684-5201
Anderson Leroy	684-2826
Anderson W H Rt 2	684-4581
Anderson Winston Rt 2	684-4544
Andrews J H Rt 1 Clns	684-2708
Archambeault I G Rt 1 Clns	684-3991
Archambeault Kirby C	684-5831
Attebery Gwen	684-3948

B

Barfield Evelyn Rt 1 Clns	684-3812
Barnard Clayton C	684-2856
Beaver Creek Plantation P O Bx 310	684-2772
Beckum T E Rt 1 Clns	684-3772

BERRY COMPANY THE

the Berry Company®

CUSTOMER SERVICE
3170 Kettering Blvd Dayton OH

Toll Free **800 877-0475**

DIVISION SALES OFFICE
1226 Eastchester Dr High Point NC

Toll Free **800 578-4333**

Beshires Eloise	684-3652
Bishop Oreta	684-4711
Blackstone Larry	684-2227
Blackstone Selwyn R Rt 1 Clns	684-3062
Bowen Delan M Rt 2	684-2060
Bowen Isaac K	684-5678
Bowen Jennifer L Rt 2 Bx 405	684-3596
Bowen Robert	684-2889
Boyette James Rt 2 Clns	684-5803
Branson Nicky & Cindy P O Bx 415	684-2746

Brantley Nikki	684-2779
Brewer Joyce & Assoc	684-2148
Brewer Joyce B	684-5419
Brooks Irene W	684-5300

BROWN BANK THE
Division of Citizens Bank
Partner of Flag Financial

684-2130

Brown Clarence Sr P O Bx 32	684-2573
Brown Danny Rt 2	684-4223
Brown George	684-3737
Brown Heath	684-4400
Brown J L Rt 2 Clns	684-2621
Brown J R	684-2731
Brown Katherine Rt 2	684-2944
Brown Randy	684-3541
Brown Randy Rt 1 Clns	684-3540
Brown Raymond Rt 1 Clns	684-3603
Brown Tommie	684-2946
Brown W L	684-2165
Brown W L (Buster) & Carolyn Jr	684-2169
Browning Clifton E Sr Cbtw	684-5406
BUDDY'S SERVICE STATION	684-2775
Bullard James R Rev & Becky Rt 1 Bx 1155	684-2756
Burgos Roberto Rt 2 Bx 310	684-2537
Burns Bruce	684-4558
Burroughs James D Jr Rt 1 Clns	684-4013
Burroughs M L Rt 1 Clns	684-5711

C

Callaway Johnny H Rt 1 Clns	684-2057
Callaway Robert Hall Rt 2 Clns	684-3373
Callaway Roy	684-4701
Calloway B H Clns	684-2053
Calloway David H	684-3370
Calloway Loran Rt 2 Clns	684-2634
Calloway Madison Clns	684-3372
Calloway Roger Jr Rt 2 Clns	684-2622
Campione Melanie Hendrix P O Bx B356	684-2282
Canady Ed	684-4233
Cannon James E II Rt 2 Bx 326	684-2736
Cardell Elaine Collins Apt	684-4637
Cartee Sandra	684-3177
Carter Cordeal Mrs	684-5371
Carter Earl Rt 2 Clns	684-2557
Castro Juan Jose Jr	684-2535
Cedar Creek Primitive Baptist Church Rt 2 Clns	684-3229
Chandler Stan Rt 1 Clns	684-4141
Charlton Grove Baptist Church Rt 2 Clns	684-3815
Christian Life Fellowship Sunlight	684-5987

-Pineland Telephone Cooperative, 2000, p. 45

TEST C: TIMED READING

Tear out this page to use for a skimming quiz. You will be skimming a page of a menu from Nick's Restaurant which can be found on the next page. Use the information you learned in this chapter about eye movement techniques to skim the menu. Write your answers in the spaces provided below. You will have 2 MINUTES and 30 SECONDS to answer the questions. Your teacher will tell you when to begin and when to put your pencil down.

1. How much are center cut pork chops?   1. _____

2. How many different fish dishes are offered?   2. _____

3. What days are two eggs any style offered?   3. _____

4. Does Nick's Restaurant serve hash browns?   4. _____

5. What kind of coffee does the restaurant provide?   5. _____

6. How much does Sunday brunch cost?   6. _____

7. What would the bill be for an order of fish & chips and Sunday brunch (excluding tax)?   7. _____

8. What comes with the pork tenderloin?   8. _____

9. What is the alternate for a pancake breakfast?   9. _____

10. Can you eat crab legs for less that $20.00 (don't include tax)?   10. _____

NICK'S RESTAURANT

*BEEF 	--- AA,AAA oven Roasted Prime Rib au jus $13.95 --- AA,AAA Alberta Char broiled N.Y Striploin $13.95 --- Tender Veal Cutlet $9.95
*PORK 	--- 1/2 Rack or Full Rack Charbroiled Ribs $9.95-$15.95 --- Pork Tenderloin with Freshly Sauteed Vegetables $13.95 --- Centre Cut Pork Chops $9.95
*CHICKEN 	--- Grilled Bonless Breast of Chicken $8.95 --- Chicken Cordon Swiss $10.25 --- 1/4 Chicken Dinner $7.95
*FISH 	--- Pan Fried Lake Erie Yellow Perch $13.95 --- Pan Fried Pickerel $13.95 --- Fish and Chips $7.99 --- Crab Legs $18.95 --- Sauteed Black Tiger Garlic Shrimp $14.95

*Reg Entrees include Soup or Salad an Steaks include choice of Sauteed Fried Onions or Mushrooms or Onion Rings.

ITALIAN 	Lasagna and Ceasar Salad and Garlic Toast $8.95 Chicken Breast Alfredo and Caesar Salad and Garlic Toast $9.75 Veal Parmesan with Spaghetti,Caesar salad and Garlic Toast $10.25 Chicken Parmesan with Spaghetti,Caesar salad and Garlic Toast $9.95

-OVER FOR MORE OF NICK'S RESTAURANT

Breakfast 	---Monday Through Saturday Two eggs any style with bacon or ham or sausage, homefries, toast, coffee and chilled juice...$3.95 ---Also available daily ---French Toast or Pancake Breakfast ---Pemeal Bacon and Eggs ---Pancakes and Eggs ---Steak and Eggs ---Three egg omelettes and much more
 **Sunday Brunch**	$6.95 15 items to choose from and serving Brazilian Canadian Coffee the best gourmet coffee around.

-Nick's Restaurant, Montreal, Canada, 2001

TEST D: TIMED READING

Tear out this sheet but do not tear out the comprehension questions' sheet. Your professor will time you. She or he will write the times (in 10-second increments) on the board as you read. Read the passage below about Koko the gorilla. When you finish the selection, look up to see the last time recorded and write your time in the space provided at the end of the selection. Then go back to the comprehension questions in your book.

Because of the research of Dr. Francine Patterson, the world has had the opportunity to see gorillas in a new light. Although her relationship with Koko was supposed to be short-term, it became a lifetime of learning. Dr. Patterson's 30-year relationship with Koko, a western lowland gorilla she taught to communicate in sign language, was indeed a remarkable one. At the time they met, Dr. Patterson was a graduate student interested in animal intelligence and Koko was a newborn struggling for life at the San Francisco Zoo. Through interviews and revealing historical footage, we have been able to see the development of this most unusual friendship which has turned out to be a landmark alliance.

Koko was born on July 4th, 1971, and she was named Hanabi-Ko, which in Japanese means "fireworks child." Koko was a weak when she was born, but she managed to pull through. Patterson, who was a psychology graduate student at Stanford University in California at the time, was able to begin working with Koko by her first birthday because she had overcome her illness and was indeed healthy. Although the plan was for Patterson to spend only a few years working with the ape in a communications experiment, they became lifelong friends.

Could a gorilla learn *American Sign Language*? This was the question which haunted Patterson. This complex set of gestures pioneered by the deaf seemed the perfect vehicle by which communication could take place. To teach Koko, Patterson would first make the sign for "eat," for example, then take Koko's hand and form the word. The gorilla was a quick learner, and her ability was phenomenal. Within weeks her vocabulary quickly grew to dozens of signs. Koko became more than a media curiosity. She challenged stereotype that gorillas were slow and stupid. In her kind, soulful eyes, millions of people saw what definitely signs of wisdom and intelligence.

Today, Koko is 30 years old and has learned more than 1,000 words; she has also shown the aptitude for other skills, in particular that of gorilla art. She has created paintings inspired by her surroundings. In fact, Koko has had something added to her environment- another gorilla! His name is Michael, and he lives with Koko. Michael also has painted; he has recently finished a portrait of his dog in black-and-white!

Koko has matured to a height of 5 feet and a weight of 300 pounds. Plans are to move her to the Maui, Hawaii where the vegetation and weather is more like her African homeland. For the present, she will stay in northern California using her ability to sign to continually amaze us. With her hands and her soulful eyes, Koko has helped us recognize that friendships can bridge and heal any communication problems.

-adapted from PBS/WNET, 2000

Time: _____   *Words Per Minute (WPM):* _____

1. You can infer from the passage that Dr. Francine Patterson is probably a(n)

a. medical doctor.
b. anthropologist.
c. psychiatrist.

2. Koko's vocabulary now consists of

a. dozens of signs for English words.
b. more than 1,000 words.
c. three words.

3. Koko now lives in

a. California.
b. Hawaii.
c. Maui.

4. When Koko was born researchers

a. were ecstatic that she was so healthy.
b. were worried Koko would die.
c. could see from her eyes she was intelligent.

5. Koko's name comes from

a. China.
b. Hawaii.
c. Japan.

6. A good title for this passage would be

a. "Humans Have Much to Learn from Chimps."
b. "The Flowering of an Unusual Relationship: A Gorilla and a Student!"
c. "How to Use American Sign Language to Teach Gorillas."

7. It can be concluded from the passage that Koko is

a. a gentle animal.
b. dangerous.
c. unable to learn.

8. The author gets the point across through the use of

a. time order, explanation, and description.
b. sequence and location.
c. analogy, comparison, and contrast.

9. "Footage," as underlined in paragraph one most nearly means

a. steps in time.
b. videos.
c. history.

10. The author's tone reveals that s/he

a. dislikes Koko.
b. is suspicious of Dr. Patterson.
c. is impressed with Koko.

Now that you have finished the comprehension questions, check the Time-Rate Conversion Chart on page 79 and write the Words Per Minute (WPM) it took you to read the passage. Write this in the space provided underneath the passage. Write your comprehension score above the passage next to "SCORE."

TIME-RATE CONVERSION CHART

Reading Time	Words Per Minute
1:00	400
1:10	345
1:20	300
1:30	265
1:40	240
1:50	220
2:00	200
2:10	185
2:20	170
2:30	160
2:40	150
2:50	140
3:00	135
3:10	125
3:20	120
3:30	115
3:40	110
3:50	105
4:00	100

CHAPTER NINE: Analytical Reasoning

TEST A

Answer the multiple-choice questions based on the content of the chapter.

1. Good thinkers

a. do not develop a "habit of analysis."
b. relate what they know to what they want to learn.
c. collect facts so that they can recall them on demand.

2. One characteristic of poor thinkers is that they are

a. sure they will always find an answer.
b. logical in their problem-solving ability.
c. unaware of relationships between information.

3. To be a good "test taker," the student must

a. think through the problems.
b. memorize the answers.
c. learn test-taking tricks.

4. In analytical reasoning, a student must

a. first find the main idea.
b. break a larger problem into smaller parts.
c. allow gaps of knowledge to exist.

5. Analytical reasoning should be applied

a. every time a student reads a textbook.
b. only when working in mathematics textbooks.
c. only when reading graphs, tables, and charts.

6. Which one of the following does *not* help a student understand the text better?

a. graphs
b. charts
c. italics

7. According to Bloom and Broder, an unsuccessful student

a. follows directions well.
b. is passive in his/her thinking.
c. is concerned with details.

8. Learning to comprehend what you read involves

a. memorizing the textbook.
b. using your intuition to arrive at answers.
c. learning to reason.

9. All of the following are characteristics of poor college readers *except*

a. sequential understanding.
b. one-shot thinking.
c. a willingness to allow gaps of knowledge to exist.

10. Reading is

a. active and passive.
b. problem solving and thinking.
c. memorizing and concentrating.

11. When analyzing chapter graphics and diagrams, it is a good idea to

a. glance over them quickly to save time.
b. read more into the graphs than supported by fact because they never give the full picture.
c. refer back and forth between the graphic and the portion in the text which discusses the graphic.

12. Graphics such as maps, tables, and charts help a student

a. visualize complex ideas.
b. comprehend the gist of the passage.
c. complicate the material being read.

13. If you are truly interested in a piece of advertising you should

a. throw it away because you might be deceived.
b. commit yourself immediately before the offer expires.
c. read the fine print to understand the offer.

14. If a student is offered a credit card, s/he should read the terms carefully because

a. credit card companies are always disreputable.
b. the interest rate may start low but change to a higher rate.
c. if you already have one card, you can't get another one.

15. Junk mail would include all of the following *except*

a. credit card applications and terms.
b. book club offers.
c. college recruitment information.

16. "Loss leaders" are

a. advertising promotions.
b. free items given in return for a consumer purchasing future merchandise.
c. a gimmick exclusively used by book clubs.

Questions 17 through 20 are based on the graph (Figure 1) below. Study the graph which portrays the numbers of intimate murder victims, then answer the multiple choice questions which follow.

FIGURE 1

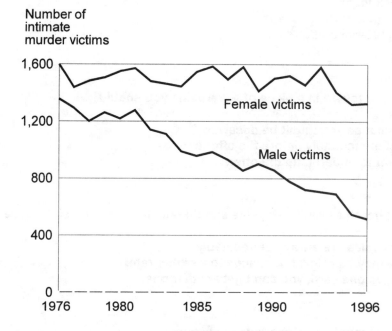

Note: Intimates include spouses, ex-spouses, common-law spouses, same sex partners, boyfriends, and girlfriends.

-U.S. Department of Justice, 2000

17. According to Figure 1, for persons murdered by intimates, the number of male victims in 1985 was about

a. 1,600.
b. 0.
c. 1,000.

18. We can infer from Figure 1 that in 1976

a. there was a dramatic difference in the number of murders by gender.
b. murders by intimates of men and women were about the same in number.
c. that the number of murders by intimates was insignificant.

19. For the purposes of the graph in Figure 1, "intimates" include all of the following *except*

a. next-door neighbors.
b. common-law spouses.
c. same-sex partners.

20. We can conclude from Figure 1 (analyzing the 1976 through 1996 statistics) that

a. there have always been more male victims than female victims.
b. the number of female victims will never decrease.
c. most likely the number of female victims will not decrease drastically in the near future.

CHAPTER TEN: Inference

Answer the multiple-choice questions based on the content of the chapter.

TEST A

1. Inferences are

a. based on suggestions that carry meaning.
b. supporting details that carry meaning.
c. actual words that carry meaning.

2. All of the following imply meaning rather than directly state it *except*

a. cartoons.
b. an almanac.
c. mysteries.

3. The best strategy for making the correct inference is to

a. first find the main idea.
b. consider the clues given within the passage.
c. re-read the passage.

4. The process of making inferences involves

a. ignoring connotations.
b. creating an outline.
c. making a connection with previous knowledge.

5. Connotations are

a. emotions surrounding a word.
b. manipulations.
c. the same as denotations.

6. **Slanted language is used to**

a. alert the reader.
b. educate the reader.
c. persuade the reader.

7. **Drawing a conclusion is**

a. literal comprehension.
b. inferential comprehension.
c. idiomatic comprehension.

8. **For the most part, idioms are used**

a. in conversation.
b. in formal writing.
c. only by groups such as cults or gangs.

9. **Which of the following is *not* a literary device?**

a. irony
b. personification
c. idiomatic usage

10. **The difference between a simile and a metaphor is that**

a. a metaphor is indirectly stated.
b. a simile uses "like" or "as" in the comparison.
c. a simile is figurative language.

TEST B

Read the story below about Hildegard, an anchoress who lived during the Middle Ages. Then, read the statements which follow. Write an "I" in the space provided if the statement is an inference. Write an "F" if the statement is a fact.

     Hildegard of Bingen (1098-1179) was a remarkable woman, a "first" in many fields. At a time when few women wrote, Hildegard produced major works of theology and visionary writings. When few women were accorded respect, she was consulted by and advised bishops, popes, and kings. She used curative powers of natural objects for healing, and wrote treatises about the medicinal uses of plants, animals, trees and stones. She is the first composer whose biography is known; she founded a vibrant convent where her musical plays were performed. Revival of interest in this extraordinary woman of the Middle Ages was initiated by musicologists and historians of science and religion.

     Hildegard was born the tenth child of a noble family. As was customary with the tenth child (which the family could not count on feeding), she was dedicated at birth to the church. The girl started to have visions of luminous objects at the age of three, but soon realized she was different and hid this gift for many years. At age eight the family sent this strange girl to an anchoress named Jutta to receive a religious education. Anchors of both sexes, though from most accounts they seem to be largely women, led an ascetic life, shut off from the world inside a small room, usually built attached to a church so that they could follow the services, with only a small window acting as their link to the rest of humanity. Food would be passed through this window and refuse taken out. After Jutta's death, when Hildegard was thirty-eight years of age, she was elected the head of the convent, living within the cramped walls of the anchorage.

-"The Life and Works of Hildegard," 2001

_____1. The author's attitude toward Hildegard is one of respect.

_____2. Hildegard was born into a noble family.

_____3. Hildegard most probably had a tutor before Jutta became her teacher.

_____4. Hildegard knew about alternative medicine techniques.

_____5. Hildegard wrote music.

In current times, women are not generally thought of as warriors. However, in Medieval times, a wife or daughter would have been expected to defend the castle against aggressors. In Scotland there was a woman born (c. 1300 - c. 1369) who was the daughter of the great Randolf, Earl of Moray. This woman was famed for her bravery. Her name was Black Agnes Randolph. She was so named because she had a dark complexion and dark hair. Black Agnes proved to be a fierce warrior when she was young and fought for de Bruce. She is better known, though, for successfully holding the Castle of Dunbar against the English enemy in 1334. The Earl of Salisbury laid siege to the castle for over five months, but Black Agnes hurled rocks and insults at the English. As a last attempt, the enemy brought Agnes's brother to the castle gates and threatened to kill him. Agnes responded by saying that if they killed her brother that would merely mean that she would become the Earl of Moray!

_____6. Agnes didn't love her brother.

_____7. Black Agnes enjoyed fighting the English enemy.

_____8. Agnes was the daughter of the great Randolf, Earl of Moray.

_____9. In 1334 Salisbury laid siege to Dunbar castle.

_____10. Black Agnes hated the English.

TEST C

After reading the passage, answer the True-False questions.

The Cold War mentality left its imprint on politics and culture during the late 1940s and early 1950s. A certain paranoia permeated the early Cold War years. The nature of the fight against Communism contributed to the paranoia. Politicians warned Americans that Communism silently and secretly destroyed a country from within. Although allegedly directed from Moscow, its aim was subversion through the slow destruction of a country's moral fiber. No one knew which institution it would next attack, or when. The politicians told Americans to watch for the unexpected, to suspect everyone and everything. As a result, between 1945 and 1955 a broad spectrum of institutions, organizations, and individuals came under suspicion.

The House of Representatives established a committee on Un-American Activities (HUAC) in the late 1930s to combat subversive right-wing and left-wing movements. Its history was less than distinguished. From the first it tended to see subversive Communists everywhere. HUAC even announced that the Boy Scouts were infiltrated by Communists. In 1947, HUAC traveled to Hollywood to investigate Communist infiltration in the film industry. The committee called a group of radical screenwriters and producers and actors into its sessions to testify. (Testimony was even given by such notable actors as Ronald Reagan.) Asked if they were Communists, a group of leftist filmmakers known as the "Hollywood Ten" refused to answer questions about their political beliefs. They believed that the First Amendment protected them. In the politically charged late 1940s, however, their rights were not protected. Those who refused to divulge their political affiliations were tried for contempt of Congress, sent to prison, and blacklisted.

-Martin, J. K., 1997, pp. 924

_____1. In general, people were paranoid of Communists during the early Cold War years.

_____2. Politicians told the public that communism only came from Moscow.

_____3. Most Boy Scouts were left-wing Communists.

_____4. Ronald Reagan was not convicted of being a Communist.

_____5. There were no consequences for the "Hollywood Ten" after they refused to testify.

While the actual teen driving provisions have been incorporated into a second bill in Georgia, the Driving Under the Influence (DUI) legislation received a healthy amount of debate. Federal law has moved the blood alcohol content to .08 for an automatic DUI. States must comply with this in order to receive federal road funding. Georgia has a floating law that allows an officer to make a determination at .08 with .10 as the absolute limit. By not changing the law, Georgia would lose up to $200 million over five years from the federal government.

The bill also added language to combat "road rage." House Bill 385 sets up the offense of aggressive driving, which will count six points against a driver's license. Aggressive driving is defined as operating a motor vehicle with the intent to annoy, harass, molest, intimidate, injure or obstruct another person. Those convicted could face up to 12 months in jail and $5,000 in fines. This bill passed overwhelmingly, 171-2.

-Barnard, 2001, p. 8

_____6. To combat road rage, Georgia House of Representatives proposed House Bill 385.

_____7. In Georgia the current blood alcohol content rating for determining intoxication is firmly set at .08.

_____8. States must comply with Federal laws in order to get funding for roads.

_____9. A conviction of aggressive driving will count six points against a driver's license in Georgia.

_____10. The author's style of writing is more entertaining than informative.

CHAPTER ELEVEN: Critical Reading

TEST A

Answer the multiple-choice questions based on the content of the chapter.

1. When you read critically, you are

a. reading for enjoyment.
b. accepting the ideas of the author without questioning them.
c. assessing the value and validity of the material.

2. If your purpose in writing an essay is to inspire, you must

a. give all the facts, whether or not they support your thesis.
b. educate and persuade the reader.
c. describe and narrate the information.

3. In reading theory, "point of view" refers to

a. an opinion on a subject.
b. the first grammatical person.
c. the narrative voice.

4. Bias is

a. a neutral stance.
b. the opposite of "point of view."
c. like prejudice.

5. The author's tone

a. is not important to comprehension.
b. describes the writer's attitude toward the subject.
c. can not be recognized by the choice of words the author uses.

6. An opinion

a. is a statement of feeling.
b. can be proved right or wrong.
c. is not an interpretation.

7. Fallacies and tricks of persuasion include all of the following *except*

a. the bandwagon.
b. circular reasoning.
c. statistical analysis.

8. In reading critically, the reader

a. must realize that the author is always right.
b. should evaluate the text.
c. is not biased, but the author is.

9. When reading critically, the reader might ask which of the following questions?

a. What are the author's credentials?
b. How many pages is the article?
c. What are the writer's hobbies?

10. In general, an editor's intent in writing an editorial is to

a. entertain.
b. narrate.
c. persuade.

TEST B

While reading the paragraphs below, write whether or not the sentence (immediately <u>before</u> the blank) is a statement of Fact (F) or a statement of opinion (O).

Fifty years after the Korean War, the U.S. government has organized several teams dedicated to finding and identifying U.S. servicemen missing in action. Each team is made up of a team leader, a noncommissioned officer in charge, an anthropologist, a mortuary affairs specialist, a medic, and a photographer. 1._____ Acting as modern-day detectives, the recovery teams are doing an excellent job. 2._____ They travel to a variety of remote and often dangerous locations, ranging from the glaciers of Tibet to the tropical jungles of New Guinea. On site, teams spend long days sifting through soil, searching for bone fragments, aircraft wreckage and personal clothing. This part of the job is the most tedious. 3._____

Army Sgt. Kenneth Nesbitt, a light-wheeled-vehicle mechanic, is a member of this team. "I've been with the organization for two months," said Nesbitt, 1985 graduate of Glennville High School. 4._____ "It's my job to maintain military and civilian vehicles in the field. This is the first time mechanics have been assigned here. I'm looking forward to having a positive impact. My work will save the military a lot of money." 5._____ Since its inception in 1973, the teams have identified the remains of 933 service men and women.

-Tarello, 2001, p. 17

In 1975 state officials found that 70 of the 150 employees in a pesticide manufacturing plant in Hopewell, Virginia had been poisoned by exposure to a pesticide used as an ant and roach poison. 6._____ In the plant, kepone dust filled the air, covered equipment, and was even found in the employees' lunch area. Some workers also brought kepone dust home on their clothes and contaminated family members. 7._____ The plant was shut down and 29 workers were hospitalized with uncontrollable shaking, slurred speech, apparent brain and liver damage, inability to concentrate, joint pain, and, in some cases, sterility. Allied Chemical Company has paid out $13 million in damage suits to the victims and their families. 8._____

In 1984 the world's worst industrial accident occurred at a Union Carbide pesticide plant located in Bhopal, India. Almost 2,700 people were killed when highly toxic methyl isocyanate gas, used in the manufacture of pesticides, leaked from a storage tank. At least 14,000 became seriously ill and suffered from blindness, sterility, kidney and liver infections, tuberculosis, and brain damage. The victims have sued for $3.1 billion in damages.

Plant safety is crucial. 9._____ These tragedies could probably have been prevented by the expenditure of perhaps no more than a million dollars. 10._____

-Miller, 1988, p. 398

TEST C

Read the paragraphs below and answer the multiple-choice questions that follow.

America and most of the civilized world has a fascination with health and beauty. When was the last time you saw a billboard or a television commercial featuring a fat, ugly person? For those of us not blessed with an attractive <u>countenance,</u> these can be very trying times.

I've had this problem for years. In fact, when I was born they called in a vet. My mother was caught two days later in the nursery trying to switch my ID bracelet with that of another child. As I was growing up, she tried the old trick of tying a pork chop around my neck so the dogs would play with me. The dogs preferred to dig for turnips in the garden instead.

When my sight started failing in grammar school and I had to get glasses, that didn't help my looks much either. My classmates always called me "D.U." That stood for "double ugly."

"Beauty is only skin deep," I would argue.

"Yeah," they would reply, "but ugly goes clear to the bone."

In the seventh grade we had a Halloween masquerade party at school. The scariest costumes were awarded prizes. The kid who placed first went as me.

-Grizzard, 1985, pp. 141-142.

1. The purpose of the selection is to

a. persuade.
b. inform.
c. entertain.

2. The author's tone is

a. humorous.
b. formal.
c. indignant.

3. As used in the selection, <u>countenance</u> most nearly means

a. visual.
b. appearance.
c. characteristic.

4. The author's bias leans toward

a. beautiful people.
b. ugly people.
c. children in costumes.

5. We can infer from the selection that the writer

a. was hurt by the comments made about his physical appearance.
b. ignored the children who made mean comments.
c. told his mother of the children who made fun of him.

Childbirth in Colonial America was a difficult and sometimes dangerous experience for women. During the seventeenth and eighteenth centuries, between 1 and 1.5 percent of all births ended in the mother's death-as a result of exhaustion, dehydration, infection, hemorrhage, or convulsions. Since the typical mother gave birth to between five and eight children, her lifetime chances of dying in childbirth ran as high as one in eight. This meant that if a woman had eight female friends, it was likely that one would die in childbirth.

Understandably, many colonial women regarded pregnancy with dread. In their letters, women often referred to childbirth as "the greatest of earthly miserys," or "that evel hour I loock forward to with dread." Many, like New England poet Ann Bradstreet, approached childbirth with a fear of impending death. In addition to her anxieties about pregnancy, an expectant mother was filled with apprehensions about the survival of her newborn child. The death of a child in infancy was far more common than it is today. In the healthiest seventeenth-century communities, 1 infant in ten died before the age of five. In less healthy environments, three children in ten died before their fifth birthday. Puritan minister Cotton Mather saw eight of his fifteen children die before reaching the age of two.

-Martin, J. K., 1997, p. 62

6. The tone of the passage is

a. academic.
b. informal.
c. nostalgic.

7. The purpose of the passage is to

a. contrast colonial childbirth to current-day childbirth.
b. inform the reader of the realities childbirth during the Colonial Era.
c. persuade the reader that men took advantage of women during the Colonial Era.

8. A colonial woman's chances of dying in childbirth were

a. one in ten.
b. one in 1.5.
c. one in eight.

9. The sentence, "In the healthiest seventeenth-century communities, one infant in ten died before the age of five," is a statement of

a. opinion.
b. fact.
c. inference.

10. The words "miserys," "evel," and "loock," are most likely

a. examples of colonial spelling.
b. misspellings.
c. typographical errors.

     By day, it was only when Katherine saw his traits in his children that she thought of the Duke. Young John looked most like him, the tawny gold hair, the arrogant grace of movement. But Harry had his voice, deep, sometimes sarcastic, sometimes so caressing that it turned her heart over. They all had his intense blue eyes, except Joan. But by night, sometimes she was with him in dreams. In these dreams there was love between them, tenderness greater than there had really been.
     She had had no direct communication with him in these years, but he had been just, as she had known he would. There had been legal documents: severance papers sent, which allowed her to keep the properties he had previously given her, and made her a further grant of two hundred marks a year for life "in recognition of her good services towards my daughters by Lady Blanche." No mention of his Beaufort children, but Katherine understood very well that this generous sum was to be expended for their benefit.
     So that was how it ended, those ten years of passionate love.

-Seton, 1954, p. 546.

11. The purpose of the passage is to

a. compare Katherine to the Duke.
b. narrate Katherine's story after her love affair.
c. describe Katherine's children.

12. The tone of the passage is one of

a. happiness.
b. heartbreak.
c. anger.

13. The word <u>just</u>, as underlined in the passage, most nearly means

a. fair.
b. only.
c. unreasonable.

14. We can infer from the passage that Katherine's oldest child

a. was about ten years old.
b. couldn't have been over three years old.
c. was an infant.

15. The passage implies that Katherine

a. detested the Duke.
b. did not love her children because they were illegitimate.
c. still longed for the Duke.

Whether you are starting or continuing on the academic road to success, there are a series of <u>markers</u> that will help you keep on the path. First, you must believe. Believe in yourself, believe in others, and believe in the process of life. You are here for a purpose. Second, keep an open mind. Be aware of things that are working and things that are not. Be willing to make changes. Third, know when you need help and be willing to ask for it. There are many people who can assist you; be specific when you ask for help. Fourth, use your resources: people, books, nature, experiences, events, travel-that which is seen and that which is unseen. Fifth, remember who you are and why you are here. Remind yourself what it is that you want to accomplish. Sixth, balance your life. There is a weariness that occurs when life's energies are out of harmony. Body, mind, and spirit need nurturing on a daily basis. Lastly, remember that storms never last.

-Hamachek, 1995, pp. 17-18

16. **The purpose of the paragraph is to**

a. motivate students.
b. discourage students.
c. reprimand students.

17. **According to the article, a student should**

a. keep to him/herself.
b. believe in him/herself.
c. use the mind more than the body.

18. **As used in the paragraph, <u>markers</u> most nearly means**

a. highlighters.
b. brands.
c. signposts.

19. **The tone of the passage is**

a. optimistic.
b. neutral.
c. pessimistic.

20. **This passage was probably written by a(n)**

a. athletic director.
b. counselor.
c. writing instructor.

CHAPTER TWELVE: Independent Textbook Assignment

TEST A: SELF-TEST

You will need a pen and a highlighter to complete this test. The passage below is presented so that you may notate the major points out to the side of the selection. You are to complete the following steps:

Step 1. Take notes as you read. Write the major points of the passage in the space provided.

Step 2. Read each comprehension question.

Step 3. When you find the answer to the question IN YOUR SIDE NOTES, highlight it; then write the correct answer for the short-answer questions. NOTE: Do not answer any question if you did not have the answer within your side notes.

Step 4. Count the number of highlights (these are the questions you would have been able to answer from your notes.)

Step 5. Give yourself a grade. (If you highlighted a word or phrase for nine out of the ten questions, give yourself a 90, and so forth.) The higher the number of highlighted items, the higher your grade would have been on a real test.

One of the most hotly debated questions in late eighteenth-century America was whether human beings were capable of improvement. Famous philosophers of the Enlightenment argued that people were naturally good and that all of society's problems could be solved by the application of reason. English philosopher William Godwin described the future in particularly glowing terms. He wrote that in the future "there would no longer be a handful of rich and a multitude of poor. . . There will be no war, no crime, no administration of justice, as it is called, and no government. Beside this there will be no disease, anguish, melancholy, or resentment."

On the other side of the debate on human perfectibility was a young Anglican Clergyman, Thomas Robert Malthus. Parson Malthus argued that human perfection was unattainable because human population growth would inevitably exceed the growth of the world's food supply. He asserted-on the basis of figures collected by Benjamin Franklin-that population tends to increase geometrically (1, 2, 4, 8) while subsistence only grows arithmetically (1, 2, 3, 4). Ultimately population would be held in check by famine, war, and disease.

_____

_____

_____

_____

_____

_____

_____

_____

_____

_____

_____

Malthus's gloomy vision of the future failed to come true because large numbers of people began to limit the number of children through the use of birth control.   Nowhere was the limitation of births more striking than in the United States. In 1800 the American birthrate was higher than the birthrate in any European nation. The typical American woman bore an average of seven children. She had her first child around the age of 23 and proceeded to bear children at two-year intervals until her early forties. Had the American birthrate remained at this level, the nation's population would have reached two billion by 1990.

Late in the eighteenth century, however, Americans began to have fewer children. Between 1800 and 1900 the birthrate fell 40 percent and even more sharply among the middle and upper classes. Where the typical mother bore seven children in 1800, the average number of children had fallen to 3.5 in 1900. And instead of giving birth to her last child at the age of 40 or later, by 1900 the typical American woman bore her last child at the age of 33. The decline of the birthrate is such an important historical breakthrough that it has its own name: *the demographic transition.*

What accounted for the declining birthrate? In part, the restriction in fertility reflected the growing realization among parents that in an increasingly commercial and industrial society children were no longer economic assets who could be productively employed in household industries or bound out as apprentices or servants. Instead, children required significant investment in the form of education to prepare them for respectable careers and marriages. The emergence of a self-conscious middle class concerned about social mobility and maintaining an acceptable standard of living also encouraged new limits on family size. The shrinking size of families also reflected a growing desire among women to assert control over their lives. Much of the impetus behind birth control came from women who were weary of an unending cycle of pregnancy, birth, nursing, and new pregnancy.

The decline in the birthrate carried far-reaching consequences for family life. First of all, motherhood and the strain of pregnancy ended earlier for women. They had an increasing number of years when young children were no longer their primary responsibility. It also meant that parents were free to invest more time, energy, and financial resources in each individual child.

-Martin, et. al, pp. 202-203

1. What was the most hotly debated question in late eighteenth century America? _____

_____

2. Who was the English philosopher involved in the debate?_____

3. Against whom was he debating?_____

4. What was the Anglican Clergyman's view on the population of the future?_____

_____

5. According to the passage, why did Malthus's prediction *not* come true?_____

_____

6. How many children (on the average) did an American woman bear during the 1800s?_____

7. In the 1900s, at what age did a woman stop having children?_____

8. What is the decline of the birthrate called?_____

9. What does the line "children were no longer economic assets" mean?_____

_____

10. Give one consequence of the decline in birthrate._____

_____

MASTERY TEST II

TEST A

Read the following selection, then answer the multiple-choice and True-False questions based on the content of the passage. Utilize the concepts and skills you have learned from your textbook in any way that you feel will aid in your comprehension of the material.

The Persian Gulf War

In August 1990, with Iraqi forces poised near the Saudi Arabian border (please refer to Map 1), the Bush administration dispatched 180,000 troops to protect the Saudi kingdom. The crisis took a dramatic turn in November 1990 when Bush doubled the number of American troops deployed in the Persian Gulf. Iraqi forces in Kuwait had climbed to 430,000 and coalition forces had to increase if Iraq was to be ejected from Kuwait by force. The President went to the United Nations for a resolution permitting the use of force against Iraq if it did not withdraw by January 15, 1991. After a heated debate, Congress also gave the President authority to wage war.

The 545,000-strong Iraqi army, the world's fourth largest, was equipped with antiship Exocet missiles, top-of-the-line Soviet T-72 tanks, and long-range artillery capable of firing nerve gas. Hussein tried to bring Israel into the war by launching Scud missiles at Israeli cities, a strategy thwarted when the United States sent Patriot antimissile missiles to Israel. A month of bombing gave the coalition forces air supremacy and destroyed thousands of Iraqi tanks and artillery pieces, supply routes and communications lines, command-and-control bunkers, and limited Iraq's ability to produce nuclear, chemical, and biological weapons. Iraqi troop morale suffered so badly during the bombing that an estimated 30 percent of Baghdad's forces deserted before the ground campaign even started.

The allied ground campaign relied on deception, mobility, and overwhelming air superiority to defeat a larger Iraqi army. The allied strategy was to mislead the Iraqis into believing that the allied attack would occur along the Kuwaiti coastline and Kuwait's border with Saudi Arabia. Meanwhile, General H. Norman Schwarzkopf, U. S. commander of the coalition forces, shifted more than 300,000 U.S., British, and French troops into western Saudi Arabia, allowing them to strike deeply in Iraq and trap Iraqi forces deep in southern Iraq and Kuwait. Only 100 hours after the ground war started, the war ended.

MAP 1

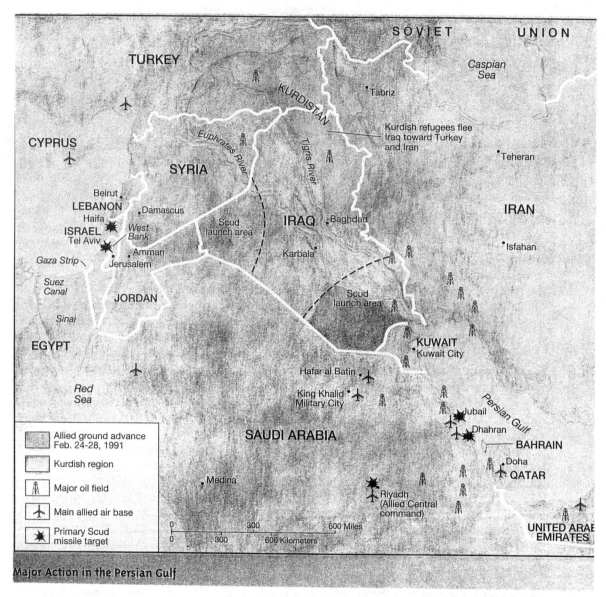

Major Action in the Persian Gulf

-Martin, 1997, pp. 1108-1109

1. During the Persian Gulf War, the U. S. president was

a. Bush.
b. Schwarzkopf.
c. related to the Saudi Arabian king.

2. The term <u>coalition</u> <u>forces,</u> as underlined in the passage, most nearly means

a. American troops.
b. Iraqi troops.
c. a combination of American, Arabian, British, and French troops.

3. The Iraqi force numbered

a. 430,000.
b. 545,000.
c. 300,000.

4. We can infer from the passage that the Iraqis obtained arms from

a. the United States.
b. Kuwait.
c. the Soviet Union.

5. The purpose of the passage is to

a. inform the reader of the developments of the Persian Gulf War.
b. persuade the reader that the allied forces were right to bomb the Iraqi forces.
c. contrast the coalition forces to the Iraqi forces.

6. It can be inferred from the passage that the Saudi Arabian government

a. tried to keep the United States from entering the war.
b. asked for assistance from the United States government.
c. remained neutral throughout the war.

7. During the Persian Gulf War, the leader of the Iraqi forces was

a. Schwarzkopf.
b. Bush.
c. Hussein.

8. It is implied in the selection that the United States Congress

a. was eager to go to war.
b. was reluctant to go to war.
c. remained neutral in regard to war.

9. As used in the passage, <u>thwarted</u> most nearly means

a. defeated.
b. victorious.
c. encouraged.

10. By reading Map 1, one can see that Iraq

a. is south of Saudi Arabia.
b. west of Syria.
c. north of Saudi Arabia.

_____11. In Map 1, one can see that Iraq had three Scud launch areas.

_____12. Map 1 shows that there were allied air bases not only in Saudi Arabia but also in Cyprus and Turkey.

_____13. It can be inferred from Map 1 that one reason Iraq wanted to overtake Kuwait was to gain oil resources.

_____14. Looking at Map 1, one can see that Iraq had easy access to the Persian Gulf.

_____15. Map 1 reveals that the Central Command Post for the allied forces was at Riyadh.

_____16. The Persian Gulf crisis began in the winter of 1991.

_____17. After being bombed by allied forces, the Iraq army was able to keep up morale.

_____18. Approximately 30%of Baghdad's forces deserted before the ground campaign started.

_____19. The allied ground campaign relied on deception, mobility, and naval superiority to defeat a larger Iraqi army.

_____20. General H. Norman Schwarzkopf took his orders from British and French military leaders.

TEST B

Answer the multiple-choice questions based on the content of the selection.

Is TV violence getting worse? If we look strictly at the amount of programming that contains violence, the numbers have not changed very much over the past 30 years. Content analyses consistently show that roughly 80% of all programs in prime time contain some kind of violence. Children's programming (e.g., Saturday morning cartoons) actually is the "worst" offender with about 94% of the shows containing violence. And children do watch a lot of television-on average, about 30 hours a week. The intensity of the violent portrayals may have increased and the availability of "pay per view" channels may have increased violent offerings, but the overall pattern has remained much the same.

The real question is not so much how much violence is on TV, but rather, what are the effects of viewing violence? Although there is some disagreement in the literature, the consistent finding is that viewing violence has a negative effect. The effect may not consist of direct imitation of some violent behavior, but is typically more subtle and results in desensitization to aggression. There are some very important qualifications to be made here; for example, the effect may be neutralized by one's ability to separate fantasy from reality. Nonetheless, we should be concerned about the level of violence in the media.

One of the major factors determining whether media violence results in enhanced aggression is the viewer's ability to separate fantasy from reality, mentioned above. If the viewer believes that the media portrayal is "real," then heightened aggression is likely to follow. However, when the viewer believes that the media image is purely fantasy, then increased aggression is far less likely. Leonard Eron has shown that a simple three-hour training program in which children are shown how special effects are used to create violence is sufficient to prevent increased media-related aggression at a one-year follow-up. So whether the World Wrestling Federation, for instance, will increase aggression in viewers or not depends, in part, on whether one sees the WWF as real or fantasy. In essence, if you realize that the violence is faked, you will not be as likely to respond in an aggressive manner.

When the violence is real (for example, a clip of a war scene on the nightly news), the effects can be the same as with fictional violence. In fact, you might argue that the effects should be more profound. First, the emotional reaction to the clip is likely to be more intense. After all, this is a real act of violence, and people are likely to feel anger, disgust, etc. To the extent that the clip produces a strong emotional response, you would predict from Excitation-Transfer theory that aggressive behavior is more likely with acts of actual violence.

It is important to remember that many factors may be operating here (for example, type of commentary, length of clip, etc.). Furthermore, TV violence leads to aggression only in those who are ready to aggress (e.g., those who are frustrated, angry, and so forth). Violence on television does not automatically trigger aggression.

Did TV violence cause Columbine? The suggestion has been made that TV violence (or violent video games) was, in fact, the cause of the Columbine shootings. There is an enormous amount of research on the effects of media violence. In general, the research indicates that media violence can influence subsequent aggression in those individuals predisposed to such behavior. What I am suggesting here is that watching media violence may increase aggression, but only in the individuals who are angry, frustrated, or have lowered inhibitions towards aggression in the first place. It is also important to remember that the effects of watching filmed violence are relatively short-lived. You may see increased aggression if it is measured relatively soon (e.g., within 30 minutes) after exposure to the media violence. This is not to say that there are no long-term effects-there are, e.g., desensitization to cues associated with violence, social learning, and so on.

So, did TV violence cause Columbine? I do not think that it is quite that simple. Some form of media violence may have influenced Harris and Klebold. However, this would not have happened in a vacuum. Violent images may have desensitized the aggression and made it seem normal. But the images would not have generated the frustration or supplied the firepower used by Harris and Klebold. Media violence by itself is not the culprit.

-Atkinson, pp. 154-156; 158-159

1. Approximately what percent of all programs in prime-time television contain some kind of violence?

a. ninety-four
b. eighty
c. one hundred

2. On average, how many hours per week do children watch television?

a. eighty
b. three
c. thirty

3. A major factor in determining whether media violence results in aggression is

a. the viewer's ability to separate fantasy from reality.
b. the level of violence in the media.
c. parental guidance.

4. According to the passage, the worst offenders in regard to television violence are

a. soap operas.
b. prime time dramas.
c. Saturday morning cartoons.

5. The author suggests that viewing violence

a. causes direct imitation of violent acts.
b. results in a desensitization to aggression.
c. separates fantasy from reality.

6. As used in paragraph one, <u>portrayals</u> most nearly means

a. enactments.
b. paintings.
c. cartoons.

7. According to the article, if an individual is ready to aggress, s/he is more likely to do so after watching

a. a news clip.
b. the World Wrestling Federation.
c. Saturday morning cartoons.

8. In regard to the Columbine shootings, the suggestion has been made that the violent acts were due to

a. video viewing.
b. TV violence.
c. peer pressure.

9. The author believes that media violence

a. is the cause of violence in our society.
b. is not solely to blame for violence in our society.
c. produces anger.

10. Which of the following is *not* mentioned as a factor in aggressive behavior?

a. conflicting personalities between teachers and students
b. type and length of news clips
c. predisposition to violence

TEST C

According to Russell (1994), millions of wives are assaulted by their husbands each year in the United States alone. When these battered women are asked why their husbands assaulted them, many have a simple answer: "Jealousy!" And growing evidence indicates that they are correct. Sexual jealousy-a perceived threat to a romantic relationship from a rival for one's partner-does appear to be a very potent cause of aggression. Individuals who feel that their lover has "done them wrong" by flirting-or worse-with another person often experience strong feelings of anger, and frequently think about or actually engage in actions designed to punish their lover, the rival, or both.

Do males and females differ in such reactions, and in the tendency to translate sexual jealousy into assaults against their spouse or lover? On the basis of the findings mentioned above, you might assume that males experience stronger jealousy and are more likely to become aggressive. And indeed, the incidence of husbands assaulting wives is much higher than the reverse. But remember: Males are generally much stronger than females and have often had much more experience with aggression. So the fact that men are more likely to assault women than vice versa doesn't necessarily mean that males experience stronger sexual jealousy; perhaps females experience jealousy that is just as strong, and have equally powerful motives to punish their mates, but they simply lack the strength or expertise to do so. In fact, the findings of several studies suggest that this may be so.

Consider an experiment conducted by de Weerth and Kalma in 1993. These researchers asked a large number of students enrolled in a social psychology course at a university in the Netherlands to indicate how they would react if they learned that their current lover was having an affair with another person. As you can see from Figure 1, females reported they would be more likely to respond with verbal and physical abuse of their lover, or to cry and demand an explanation. In contrast, males indicated that they would be more likely to get drunk.

FIGURE 1

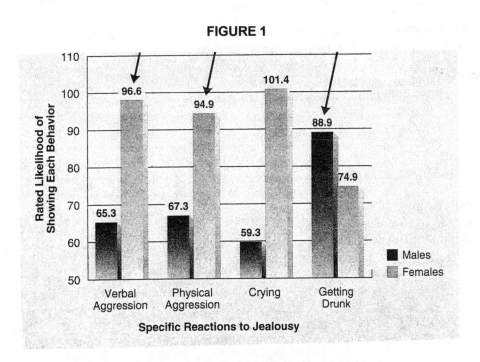

What accounts for this gender difference? One possibility is suggested by the perspective of evolutionary psychology. According to this perspective, contrasting biological forces may underlie male and female sexual jealousy. For females, such jealousy may focus primarily on the potential loss of resources needed for child rearing. Throughout most of human evolution, females have been dependent on males for the resources needed to raise children. In this context, the result would be that females would react very strongly to male sexual infidelity. For males, in contrast, sexual jealousy may rest primarily on concern over paternity. If their mate has sexual relations with other men, they may find themselves in the uncomfortable situation of raising other men's children. In the past, this was a strong basis for male sexual jealousy.

This is only one possible explanation. Whatever the precise explanation, it is clear that sexual jealousy is a strong impetus to aggression for both genders.

-Baron, 1999, pp. 356-357

1. The topic of the passage is related to

a. differences in men and women.
b. male aggression due to sexual jealousy.
c. sexual jealousy of males and females.

2. The author supports his thesis by using

a. explanation and statistics.
b. contrast and comparison.
c. persuasion.

3. According to the Weerth and Kalma study, upon finding out that their mate had sexual relations with another person, females are more likely to

a. get drunk than males.
b. respond with physical abuse than males.
c. do nothing.

4. We can infer from the passage that sexual jealousy

a. is a prevalent feeling.
b. plays no part in a relationship.
c. is the cause of many homicides.

5. According to the passage, one possible explanation for the gender difference concerning sexual jealousy is

a. social psychology.
b. child rearing.
c. evolutionary psychology.

6. The author states that for males, sexual jealousy rests primarily on

a. feeling dependent on the woman.
b. concern over paternity.
c. the damage done to their ego.

7. The tone of the passage is

a. sarcastic.
b. informal.
c. academic.

8. The word <u>impetus</u>, as used in the last sentence, most nearly means

a. motivation.
b. deterrent.
c. denial.

9. Figure 1 shows that when males are jealous they will most likely

a. cry.
b. become verbally aggressive.
c. get drunk.

10. It can be inferred from Figure 1 that when males are jealous they

a. are more physically aggressive than females.
b. will most likely cry and become verbally aggressive.
c. are more likely to "hold in" their emotions.

ANSWER KEYS

FOR

CHAPTER TESTS AND MASTERY TESTS

CHAPTER ONE: Student Success

TEST A

1. c
2. b
3. a
4. a
5. c
6. a
7. b
8. a
9. c
10. b
11. b
12. c
13. a
14. c
15. b
16. a
17. c
18. a
19. a
20. b

TEST B

Essay: Answers will vary.

CHAPTER TWO: Stages of Reading

TEST A

1. c
2. a
3. b
4. c
5. b
6. b
7. c
8. a
9. c
10. a
11. b
12. a
13. a
14. c
15. b
16. c
17. a
18. b
19. a
20. b

TEST B

1. b
2. c
3. a
4. c
5. b
6. a
7. a
8. c
9. b
10. a

CHAPTER THREE: Vocabulary

TEST A

1. a
2. b
3. b
4. c
5. b
6. c
7. a
8. c
9. c
10. c
11. b
12. a
13. c
14. b
15. a
16. b
17. b
18. c
19. a
20. c

TEST B

1.	F	11.	F
2.	T	12.	T
3.	F	13.	F
4.	F	14.	T
5.	T	15.	F
6	T	16.	T
7.	F	17.	T
8.	F	18.	T
9.	T	19.	F
10.	F	20.	F

CHAPTER FOUR: Main Idea

TEST A

1. b
2. c
3. a
4. c
5. c
6. b
7. c
8. a
9. b
10. c

TEST B

1. a
2. a
3. b
4. c
5. b
6. a
7. c
8. b
9. c
10. a

CHAPTER FIVE: Supporting Details and Organizational Patterns

TEST A

1. c
2. c
3. a
4. b
5. c
6. a
7. b
8. a
9. c
10. a
11. c
12. b
13. c
14. c
15. b
16. a
17. c
18. a
19. c
20. b

TEST B

1. c
2. a
3. b
4. b
5. c
6. a
7. a
8. b
9. c
10. c

CHAPTER SIX: Textbook Learning

TEST A

1. T
2. F
3. F
4. T
5. T
6. F
7. T
8. F
9. T
10. F
11. T
12. F
13. T
14. T
15. F
16. T
17. F
18. T
19. F
20. T

TEST B

Answers will vary.

MASTERY TEST I

TEST A

1. d
2. l
3. p
4. q
5. h
6. e
7. k
8. o
9. c
10. w
11. m
12. r
13. n
14. f
15. t
16. a
17. b
18. v
19. g
20. s
21. i
22. x
23. u
24. j
25. y

TEST B

1. b
2. a
3. c
4. c
5. c
6. F
7. F
8. T
9. T
10. T

TEST C

1. b
2. a
3. b
4. c
5. a
6. b
7. c
8. a
9. b
10. c

CHAPTER SEVEN: Test-Taking Strategies

TEST A

1. c
2. b
3. a
4. b
5. c
6. a
7. b
8. a
9. c
10. b
11. a
12. a
13. b
14. c
15. b
16. b
17. a
18. c
19. c
20. a

TEST B

1. b
2. c
3. c
4. a
5. b
6. c
7. a
8. b
9. b
10. c

TEST C

1. F TIP: the "100 percent" word *always* (indicates a false answer)
2. T TIP: the qualifying word *sometimes* (indicates a possible true answer)
3. F TIP: half the statement is true, but half is false (therefore the answer is false)
4. T TIP: cancel out the double negative
5. b TIP: elimination of two synonymous answers
6. c TIP: elimination of two synonymous answers
7. a TIP: the grammar particle "an" (indicates the answer begins with a vowel)
8. c TIP: use information that was given in a previous question
9. b TIP: nonsensical option "viruses"
10. a TIP: the longer sentence is sometimes the answer

CHAPTER EIGHT: Efficient Reading

TEST A

1. c
2. b
3. a
4. b
5. c
6. a
7. b
8. b
9. c
10. a

TEST B

1. Cobbtown
2. No
3. 14, including the Brown Bank
4. 684-2775
5. C
6. Buster
7. 684-5371
8. 3
9. Bullard
10. B356

TEST C

1. $9.95
2. 3
3. Monday through Saturday
4. No
5. Brazilian Canadian
6. $6.95
7. $14.94
8. Vegetables
9. French Toast
10. Yes

TEST D

1. b
2. b
3. a
4. b
5. c
6. b
7. a
8. a
9. b
10. c

CHAPTER NINE: Analytical Reasoning

TEST A

1. b
2. c
3. a
4. b
5. a
6. c
7. b
8. c
9. a
10. b
11. c
12. a
13. c
14. b
15. c
16. b
17. c
18. b
19. a
20. c

CHAPTER TEN: Inference

TEST A

1. a
2. b
3. b
4. c
5. a
6. c
7. b
8. a
9. c
10. b

TEST B

1. I
2. F
3. I
4. F
5. F
6. I
7. I
8. F
9. F
10. I

TEST C

1. T
2. F
3. F
4. T
5. F
6. T
7. F
8. T
9. T
10. F

CHAPTER ELEVEN: Critical Reading

TEST A

1. c
2. b
3. a
4. c
5. b
6. a
7. c
8. b
9. a
10. c

TEST B

1. F
2. O
3. O
4. F
5. O
6. F
7. F
8. F
9. O
10. O

TEST C

1. c	11. b
2. a	12. b
3. b	13. a
4. b	14. a
5. a	15. c
6. a	16. a
7. b	17. b
8. c	18. c
9. b	19. a
10. a	20. b

CHAPTER TWELVE: Independent Textbook Assignment

Answers will vary.

MASTERY TEST II

TEST A

1. a
2. c
3. b
4. c
5. a
6. b
7. c
8. b
9. a
10. c
11. F
12. T
13. T
14. F
15. T
16. F
17. F
18. T
19. F
20. F

TEST B

1. b
2. c
3. a
4. c
5. b
6. a
7. a
8. b
9. b
10. a

TEST C

1. c
2. a
3. b
4. a
5. c
6. b
7. c
8. a
9. c
10. c

REFERENCES

CHAPTER ONE

Arthur, Linda L. *Making the Most of Your Southern Experience*. Needham Heights, MA: Simon & Schuster, 1996.

Goleman, Daniel. *Healing Emotions: Conversations with the Dalai Lama*. Boston: Shambhala, 1997.

CHAPTER TWO

Martin, J K, et. al. *America and Its Peoples*. 3rd ed. New York: Longman, 1997.

Ross, George R. *Treating Adolescent Substance Abuse: Understanding the Fundamental Elements*. Boston: Allyn and Bacon, 1994.

CHAPTER THREE

Webster's New World Dictionary, David B Guralnik (ed.). 2nd edition. New York: Simon and Schuster, 1982.

CHAPTER FOUR

"Advertising Basics," Internet address: www.allbusiness.com, 2001.

Barash, David P. *Understanding Violence*. Boston: Allyn and Bacon, 2001.

DeVito, Joseph A. *Human Communication: The Basic Course*. Eighth edition. New York: Longman, 2000.

Fraser, Antonia. *The Lives of the Kings and Queens of England*. New York: Alfred A. Knopf, 1975.

Null, Gary. *Ultimate Anti-Aging Program*. New York: Kensington Books, 1999.

Peck, M. Scott. *The Road Less Traveled*. New York: Simon & Schuster, 1978.

Phadnis, Chitra. "Resumes from U.S. deluge Web sites of Indian Companies." *Financial Daily*, March 22, 2001. Internet address: www.hindubusinessline.com

Wilkins, David G, Bernard Schultz, and Katheryn M Linduff. *Art Past, Art Present*. 2nd edition. Englewood Cliffs: Prentice Hall, Inc., 1994.

CHAPTER FIVE

Barash, David P. *Understanding Violence*. Boston: Allyn and Bacon, 2001.

Bartollas, Clemens and Larry D. Hahn. *Policing in America*. Boston: Allyn and Bacon, 1999.

Bowen, John R. *Religions in Practice: An Approach to the Anthropology of Religion*. Boston: Allyn and Bacon, 1998.

Danziger, James N. *Understanding the Political World: A Comparative Introduction to Political Science.* New York: Longman, 1998.

Goldberg, Tricia. "Eating Disorders." http://www.eatingdisorders.about.com, 2001.

Meade, Marion. *Stealing Heaven: The Love Story of Heloise and Abelard.* New York: Soho Press, 1979.

Miller, G Tyler. *Environmental Science.* 2nd edition. Belmont, CA: Wadsworth, 1988.

CHAPTER SIX

Palmer, Helen. *The Enneagram.* New York: Harper and Row, 1988.

Riso, Don Richard. *Understanding the Enneagram.* Boston: Houghton Mifflin Company, 1990.

Schwartz, Tony. "Funny, you don't look twoish." *Esquire, 123,* no. 3, 1995.

Wall, James M. "By the numbers." *Christian Century, 113,* no. 3, 1996.

MASTERY TEST I

Baron, Robert A. *Essentials of Psychology.* 2nd edition. Boston: Allyn and Bacon, 1999.

Christopher, Robert C. *The Japanese Mind.* New York: Fawcett Columbine, 1983.

CHAPTER EIGHT

Pineland Telephone Cooperative. *Pineland Telephone Phone Book.* Metter Georgia, August 2000. Dayton: L. M. Berry & Co., 2000.

"Nick's Restaurant, Montreal Canada." Internet address: http://www.READTHEMENU.COM, 2001.

WNET/PBS. "A Conversation With Koko." From The Nature Series #13. New York: WNET, 2000. Internet address: http://www.pbs.org/wnet/nature/koko/friendship.html

CHAPTER NINE

U.S. Department of Justice, Office of Justice Programs. "Violence by Intimates," January 11, 2000. Internet address: http://www.ojp.usdoj.gov/bjs/abstract/vi.html

CHAPTER TEN

Barnard, Terry Representative. "Capitol Update." Claxton, Georgia: *The Claxton Enterprise,* March 8, 2001.

Martin, J K, et. al. *America and Its Peoples.* 3rd ed. New York: Longman, 1997.

"The Life and Works of Hildegard von Bingen (1098-1179)." Internet Address: http://tweedledee.ucsb.edu/ %7Ekris/music/Hildegard

CHAPTER ELEVEN

Grizzard, Lewis. *Shoot Low, Boys-They're Ridin' Sheltand Ponies*. New York: Ballantine Books, 1985.

Hamachek, Alice L. *Coping With College: A Guide for Academic Success*. Boston: Allyn and Bacon, 1995.

Martin, J K, et. al. *America and Its Peoples*. 3rd ed. New York: Longman, 1997.

Miller, G Tyler. *Environmental Science*. 2nd edition. Belmont, CA: Wadsworth, 1988.

Seton, Anya. *Katherine*. New York: Houghton Mifflin, 1954.

Tarello, Elaine. "Local residents assist in recovery of MIA service members." Reidsville, Georgia: *The Tattnall Journal*, January 11, 2001.

CHAPTER TWELVE

Martin, J K, et. al. *America and Its Peoples*. 3rd ed. New York: Longman, 1997.

MASTERY TEST II

Atkinson, Michael. *Ask Dr. Mike: Frequently Asked Questions About Psychology*. Boston: Allyn and Bacon, 2001.

Baron, Robert A. *Essentials of Psychology*. 2nd edition. Boston: Allyn and Bacon, 1999.

Martin, J K, et. al. *America and Its Peoples*. 3rd ed. New York: Longman, 1997.

NOTES

NOTES

NOTES

NOTES

NOTES

NOTES